*New York Times* **Bestselling Author**

# LAURELL K. HAMILTON

### The World of **ANITA BLAKE, VAMPIRE HUNTER**

An Ace Book / published by arrangement with the author

PRINTING HISTORY
Ace edition / September 2001

# CONTENTS

# THE ANITA BLAKE ENTERTAINMENT GUIDE

LAURELL K. HAMILTON

If you come to St. Louis some dark, humid, summer night drive towards the river, drive until you almost run out of land, then good luck on the parking. I can't help you there. Just up from the shining darkness of the water, not too far at all, is Guilty Pleasures. It's a strip club, specializing in male exotic dancers, but no humans. Vampires glide across the stage, and we can judge for ourselves if the sex appeal is all hype, or not. Sometimes you'll see a werewolf, or a wereleopard, on stage, and they don't stop at just the clothes, they shapeshift in plain sight, so we can see that unlike movie monsters, real wereanimals are very male indeed.

If you're in the mood for laughing rather than titillation, try The Laughing Corpse, it's a little drive, but not too far. Vampire comedians try to get laughs instead of screams, and there is no straighter straight-man than a zombie. Circus of the Damned is a complete carnival with rides, games, cotton candy, and circus acts that run high to monsters and beings you've only read about in mythology. Come see zombies raised from the grave, nightly. See a snake charmer work her wiles on a cobra big enough to swallow a small car. You can even bring the kids, though I'm not sure I would.

The Lunatic Cafe is a restaurant run by werewolves, though most customers never learn what goes on in the sound-proof back room. If you want to leave St. Louis, try Rawhead and Bloody Bones Bar and Grill near Branson, Missouri. One night a week is lover's night where one of the owners will cast a spell upon you to make you beautiful or handsome. Make love while the spell lasts and don't spend the night, for waking up in the morning without the magic will add a whole new meaning to "rude awakening." Danse Macabre is the newest dance club in St. Louis. Come dance with vampires, werewolves, wereleopards, and other things. If you're wanting a more family-oriented evening try Burnt Offerings. The decor in this steakhouse runs to old monster movies with waiters and waitresses dressed up like mummies, rubber-masked werewolves, vampires with big rubber fangs. Highly recommended if you've got kids.

If you're in the wilds of Tennessee far from the tourist-y areas try staying at the Blue Moon Motel, actually separate cabins. The place is owned and run by the local werewolf pack, but if you're lucky you'll never see anything they don't want you to see. If you're not so lucky, well, how much insurance you got? In Albuquerque, New Mexico, drop in at Obsidian Butterfly. Expect to see werejaguars, vampires, and authentic Aztec ritual, or as authentic as the local police will allow. In the rooms under the club you can see things that the police don't know about.

Welcome to the world of Anita Blake, where things are not what they seem, and stumbling through the wrong door, at just the right moment, can make your nightmares, or your dreams, reality.

# DEATH & SEX: A CONVERSATION WITH LAURELL K. HAMILTON

CHARLES N. BROWN
Copyright by *Locus* Publications

*Laurell K. Hamilton was born Laurell Kaye Klein, February 19, 1963 in a small town near Shirley, Arkansas. She went to Marion, a Christian college in Indiana, and received degrees in English and Biology. She currently lives in the St. Louis area.*

*Her first novel, the fantasy* Nightseer, *appeared in 1992. The next year, her long-running dark fantasy mystery series featuring vampire killer Anita Blake began with* Guilty Pleasures *(1993). That series continued with* The Laughing Corpse *(1994),* Circus of the Damned *(1995),* The Lunatic Cafe *(1996),* Bloody Bones *(1996),* The Killing Dance *(1997),* Burnt Offerings *(1998), and* Obsidian Butterfly *(2000).*

"A lot of the fans want me to be Anita Blake for them. They want me to have the same background. Anita's from the Midwest, but she's from a higher economic background than I am. She's never been poor. I was raised with just my grandmother. I'm older than everyone keeps thinking I am. I was born near Shirley, Arkansas. My family, for many generations, had been Scots-Irish hill people. I'm so white-bread, if you cut me I'd bleed bleached flour! I have no ethnicity to me, and I've always wanted some.

"By the time I was six months old, my father and mother were divorced. I don't remember him. My mother moved back in with *her* mother, my grandmother, who took care of me while my mother worked. My earliest memories of anywhere I lived were Indiana, because they'd moved up North by then. The house where I spent most of my growing-up years is across from a bean field or a cornfield, depending on the year, since they switched back and forth. The town is so small, when I was interviewed by a Chicago paper, they called it a 'hamlet,' because they could not find it on any of the atlases.

"So I'm the proverbial middle-of-nowhere, very small town writer. People I grew up with, just a year older than me, say, 'How did you come up with Anita? Why do you do this and I don't?' As far back as I can remember, I have been making up stories. I didn't write stories until I was twelve and a half—and I know it was twelve and a half, because all my characters were exactly my age for years and years. I started off like everyone else does, slogging but having a compulsion to put words on paper. I didn't write or read horror or fantasy, other than children's fantasy, until I was in my teens. Then I read Robert E. Howard's 'Pigeons From Hell' in a collection, and the moment I read it I knew, not only did I want to be a writer, but this was what I wanted to write.

"One of the turning points of my life was that my mother died when I was six. She went off to work one day and never came back. Car accident. It was very abrupt, very unexpected. I'm now older than my mother ever was by quite some years. She was 29 when she died. It was a profound lesson. I learned that not only do the people I love die, but that other adults couldn't keep them safe. It was a lesson that really stuck with me. For years, I thought it was my mother's death that made me look at the macabre, but in recent years I've looked back and realized, as far back as I can remember, when I played, I always had to play scary stuff. I came that way.

"At five, I was begging to stay up to watch Boris Karloff in *Frankenstein*. My grandmother thought she'd fool me by saying I could stay up and watch it by myself, with only one light on. I got to the point where Igor is torturing the monster with the torch, and I turned off the light, ran, turned off the TV, and dived into bed. But from that moment on, I was allowed to pretty much watch and read whatever I was able to handle. I value that a great deal.

"What we remember, and how we choose to remember it, has a great deal to do with who we are. I have to work at remembering the good, not being pessimistic. I'll remember the darker stuff, while other people I know remember the lighter stuff. It's just the way you look at the world.

"I graduated from Oak Hill High School, a very small school. I was very lucky to have some very good English teachers. One of them read one of my first stories and told me it scared her. As a shy 14-year-old, that I could scare an adult was quite heady stuff! I was in drama and on the speech team in high school, and it's stood me in very good stead, as time has gone on, to be able to project to a room, not lose my voice. What school does best is teach you how to think. It's not what you learned, it's how you learn to work with your mind.

"I went on to Marion College, which is now Indiana Wesleyan University. Interesting choice—a Christian college. It was close to home, so I could stay with my grandmother and drive back and forth. But I was asked to leave the writing program because I was a 'corrupting influence' on the other students. Now I've gone off and written exactly what my teacher there feared I would write! As far as she's concerned, I *am* corrupting people. I have her to thank for the fact that I have a biology degree as well as an English degree.

"After I graduated, I lived in Los Angeles for almost three years. *That* was certainly an interesting experience—going from where a big town was 60-70,000 people, straight to L.A. I moved from California to St. Louis, and I've lived in St. Louis around 15 years now with my family—my daughter Trinity, my partner Jonathon, and one pug.

"My daughter insists on her whole name, Trinity Diane Hamilton. She's six, and she is one of the joys of my life. I waited a long time to have her. It's a great time to have a child. My thirties are a great deal better than my twenties. I wasn't good at being in my twenties. Most people aren't. You spend them scrambling around trying to figure out who you are and what you want.

"Around 30, if you're lucky, you've figured things out, and then you kind of relax a little. Somewhere in your thirties, you finally get to that point where you not only realize life's not perfect, but that it's not supposed to be, and that's OK. I like being the age I am. I've never been happier. There's nothing else I've wanted to do but write.

"I lived in corporate America for a while when I was in L.A. I was an art editor for Xerox, if you can believe it. I'd interviewed for a text editing job, but they need someone in the Art Department. I can't draw! Eventually some client figured this out, and got quite heated about it. I got downsized during the company's restructuring. I was about halfway through my first book at that point, so I decided to just take the time to finish it. And that was the last day job I had.

"One of the reasons I write fantasy and science fiction and horror is that it is a distancing device, a step back. Also, I find real life fairly depressing. In real life, if you cross the street and get hit by a truck, it's not a big plot. In fiction, with a plot, somebody had it in for you. You can hunt them down and have your vengeance. I like that about fiction. When I write, I try to put order into chaos, to make sense of things. One of my themes is dealing with death and loss. The other is corruption. What happens when you have a good person dealing with bad things? How do they deal with it? What happens to them?

"I love Anita dearly, but she *is* a pain. She's still in that twenties mindset where no matter how cynical [she] is, she still believes it will all work out. When she first started out in the books, she was very much me at 24. That was how old I was when I wrote *Guilty Pleasures*. At 24, Anita believed the world was very black and white, good and evil. It wasn't hard. Vampires were dead, you killed them, there was no conscience problem. As the series has progressed, she's not so clear on what black and white, good and evil, is. It's grayer. And it should be. She has a higher kill count than most combat veterans, and certainly more than most police who have been on the job for years. And every day, she's been killing things that look human. You can say whatever you want, but in my world it's hard to really differentiate strongly. My vampires don't look like monsters *per se*. They look human. Especially when they're asleep in their coffins, they look like ordinary people. So Anita takes a certain amount of risk with her own psyche when she takes them out. And she is certainly suffering from that.

"One of the things that I've learned to do in the last few

years is interview people for research. You read first, to get an overview of wherever it is, and then you go and talk to your experts. I've learned how to listen. It's not my natural bent, but you *have* to. It's been very interesting, not just from what I've learned but in how I've learned it. I'm a good listener now.

"I interviewed combat veterans, and talked to police as well. When a friend of mine was assigned to a really bad neighborhood in Indianapolis as a policeman, I watched him have to lose parts of himself just to be able to keep going. He loves being a cop, but it has changed him. I talked to one Vietnam combat veteran who still, on bad nights, sleeps under the coffee table. People have been very generous with their time, generous in talking and sharing. I found that the greatest gift I can give them is the fact that I listen, I make no judgments, and I'm not horrified. But I do not interview people who kill people for sport. I have no interest in that. I have gotten a couple of letters from people who fall into that category. In a strange way, they've paid me a very high compliment. They've said I write about what it's really like to kill people. But you never answer those letters!

"A lot of people with backgrounds in Special Forces and police work are used to people, especially women, being horrified. It's a gift, to be able to listen to the worst thing this person has, let them share that, and they know it's a safe place to do that. And it has helped me make Anita real—to make her angst real, her pangs of conscience real, her spiraling down to sociopathy. Because to do what she does, she has to give up pieces of herself. You either stop and get another job, or you lose things, or you go nuts.

"When I was working on book ten, (*Narcissus in Chains*), one of the things I was really looking at was, was it too late to stop being a sociopath? Had Anita already gone over that line, and could never go back? In the next few books, she will be sitting down and saying, 'All right, I am a sociopath, but I'm going to try and act as though I'm not one.' The thing is, can you stop if you're still living the lifestyle that caused you to become a sociopath in the first place? It's not like she's a combat vet sent back home, or a policeman that changed jobs. If she keeps the same job, can she come back over the line? I don't know.

"That is the theme of most everything I've written: How a person reacts to making hard choices, real choices, and having to deal with that. I find that fascinating.

"I love my fans, because they cover such wide demographics. They go from everything from teens to 50+. I have a wide following among people—especially men—who have a violent background, military or police or whatever. A lot of the men say they don't read horror or fantasy, but they read my books. And I have a wide romance following.

"I really fought the idea that there was going to be any romance at all in the Anita books. I screamed loud and long that I wasn't going to do that. How trite. Everyone's done that. Still, she ended up in a love triangle with Richard and Jean-Claude. I'm at the point now where I don't care which one she chooses—just choose somebody!

"I've been told by one mystery editor that if I were writing straight mystery, I could not get away with the level of violence or the level of sex I do in the Anita books, because I'm a woman and my first-person protagonist is also female. If I was a man, the level of violence and the sexual content would be no problem, but because I'm a woman, they wouldn't be able to sell it. I'm a woman who is comfortable with sexuality, and that's almost not allowed still. What I write is good girl stuff. We've had good guy sex for years in fiction, especially the hardboiled detective. You just go there and you get fireworks, boom! So I do good girl sex.

"One of the reasons I write as fast as I do is because I want to read what happens next! I will start out and know the main mystery, some of the things that happen in the middle, and the end. Usually I'll know who dunnit, or *what* dunnit. But I don't know the bridge things, the relationship things. I write like I'm building across a great big chasm. I put three boards out so I can see a little further, then I put three more boards out, and that's how I get across. Often, I will write scenes where Anita has a choice—A, B, or C. I write hundreds and hundreds of pages that never see daylight. Some of them were beautiful scenes that I hold dear to my heart, but I'm not the one in charge. It's Anita trying to figure things out!

"When my first published novel, *Nightseer*, which was a much more traditional fantasy, in the vein of Robert E. Howard meets Tolkien, did not make a go of it, I decided I needed to do something different. I read mysteries for the first time, hard-boiled detective fiction, and I wanted to do that, but I still wanted to write genre—fantasy and horror. I gave Anita all my favorite toys—monster movies, folklore...all the things I wanted to play with. In hardboiled detective fiction, men get to cuss, kill people, and have sex on stage. The woman didn't get to cuss, if they killed people they had to feel really, really bad about it, and they had sex only offstage. I wanted to have a character that was tougher than the men, had a higher kill count, and could just kick butt, because I wanted to make this deficit go away. I wanted equality. And I've certainly done that.

"To do all these things, I had to mix the real world with the fantastic. And I love mixing them! Most writers take the ordinary and make it extraordinary. I take the extraordinary and make it ordinary. I love writing about Nikes and Oreos. And it's a cheat! When you're writing high fantasy or horror fantasy, you have to figure out what 14th-century underwear looked like. I couldn't get my characters in *Nightseer* undressed, because I didn't know that! But with writing in a 'now' setting, I can just say 'Nikes,' 'jeans,' and people have a frame of reference. That allows me to not spend paragraphs explaining things, and I can get on with the plot, the action, the character development. I don't have to work at the culture as much, because the culture is almost a given.

"Having said that, though, the fantastic elements change the culture. I love the fact that in my world, they're still arguing about vampires being legal citizens. Does that mean you're a bigamist if you remarry when your husband's been declared alive again? Do you have to give back your inheritance? Vampires are a given—now what? That is the real heart of science fiction. You take a supposition and go, 'Now what?' If I had to do it over again, I think Anita's world would diverge a little more from ours. But what I did when I first started the series was say, 'What if you got up tomorrow and everything that goes bump in the night was real, how would you deal with it?' That was my stepping-off point, my jumping-off-the-cliff point!

"Anita is a better girl than most of the fictional private detectives in straight mystery. Even if she's not really comfortable being a girl, she gets to do girl stuff—go shopping, eat sweet stuff....And in *Obsidian Butterfly*, when she sees one enigmatic character's house for the first time, she takes her time, really looks at it. She enjoys the experience of it. If she was a guy, she'd have to come in and be tough and not be able to look around. She literally admits to herself, because she's a girl she gets to do this. She's going to satisfy her curiosity. She doesn't have to be cool about this. It is different. It allows you parameters you don't get as a man, in this culture.

"And it's one of the reasons Anita has such a high body count too. She doesn't play fair. She has her rules, but if somebody's trying to kill her, she wants to come out the other side alive. She's smaller, she has less muscle mass, so she considers being better armed just good sense. She has a different perspective than the men do. I can explore that in the series, and people will let me get away with it.

"Mixing the genres allows me to do the best of everything I want to do. Doing the romance, I get to do as much erotic content or relationship content as I want. When I realized, books and books in, that Anita was finally going to do the dirty deed on paper, I called up friends who write romance and said, 'OK, what's out there?' (The last romance I'd read had been a Harlequin I read in junior high.) They were very kind, gave me some titles, told me what pages to read. And I learned some stuff! I had no idea romances were being written to that level of detail! So that gave me the courage to be able to write what needed to be written. Otherwise, I think I might have been a bit timid about it.

"I have to admit that originally I wanted every kiss and every caress to be so good, Anita would never have to have sex on the page. By the time I realized I was going to *have* to do that on paper, I'd written myself into a corner, because I'd spent books not flinching on the violence. What did it say about me that instead I flinched at the sex scenes? But then, that was very American. Now the camera stays on all the action, and it's a first-person point of view, because Anita is my camera, she's my eyes.

"The romance gives me the erotic content, the relationship content. The mystery is usually the skeleton of the book, my plot. But the horror allows me to do the violence level that needs to be there. I love reading cozy mysteries by writers who can have as many bodies falling out of the closet as they want, and you still have a good time—but I can't do that. When a body falls on the ground in my books, it's a tragedy. And like all good murder scenes, usually your best clues are the bodies.

"What happens in real life influences how I think about things in books. My vampires are minorities. They have no rights, and at one point you could kill them on sight. There's no other minority in this country, I *hope*, that you've been able to say that about. Now they've gotten quite far. After centuries of secrecy, they can come out. I still want Anita to go to Washington, DC. I've got a plot set there, people talking before committees about rights and death. I'm looking forward to that. But Anita's world is big because *our* world's big. One book plot will lead to another, and ideas that I didn't know I had. I have no plans to stop because I keep having more book ideas. And I'm still having a wonderful time.

"Because I enjoy writing the books as much as I do, there's a danger in there of losing everything else. But my research actually gets me out. It makes me have to look at other things. It's certainly broadened my world. I've talked to people about topics I would never have experienced myself.

"I like having my books out there, and I like having fans. I love sharing. I love genre. Now that I'm more successful, publishers are trying to mainstream me, but I'm unabashedly genre. It's what I like to read, what I like to write."

# ANITA BLAKE'S LIFE SO FAR...

**M**y name is Anita Blake. My life used to be simple. I draw a paycheck from Animators Inc. bringing the dead back to life, temporarily. So that rich Uncle Harry could say where he hid the new will, that sort of thing. I'm pretty good at it, so I see a lot of zombies on the job.

Off the job, I killed vampires. Legally. Since the Supreme Court granted the undead legal rights, your average Joe can't just go out and stake them. You need a license and a warrant. And a lot of skill. The vamps call me the Executioner. Then the cops recruited me to consult to the Regional Preternatural Investigation Team. That brought me up and close and personal with the worst of the creatures of the night. Rogue animators, overripe zombies, deranged vampires, ancient Celtic monsters, and sadistic shapeshifters.

All of which filled my days—and nights—with murder, mayhem. And monsters. Some of which I got to know. Too well.

Like Jean-Claude, the Master Vampire of the City. He claims to love me. If something that doesn't have a heartbeat can love. And Richard, the handsome schoolteacher—who turned out to be an Alpha Werewolf. He proposed once, but we broke up when I saw him eat someone. Fact is, these days my life is a cross between a preternatural soap opera and an action adventure movie. Sort of "As the Casket Turns" meets *Rambo*.

This is my world. Welcome to it. And these are my stories.

## GUILTY PLEASURES

Vampires call me The Executioner. What I call them isn't repeatable. But now a serial killer is murdering vampires—and the most powerful bloodsucker in town wants me to find the killer.

## THE LAUGHING CORPSE

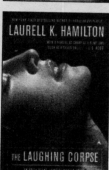

Working for Animators, Inc. is just a job—like selling insurance. But all the money in the world wasn't enough for me to take on the particular job Harold Gaynor was offering. Raising a zombie that old requires a human sacrifice, and that's one place I don't want to go. But somebody else did, though—a rogue animator. Now he's not just raising the dead . . . he's raising Hell. And it's up to me to stop it...

## CIRCUS OF THE DAMNED

As if it wasn't enough that the Master Vampire of the City was wooing me, now a tall, dark, and dangerous vampire named Alejandro has hit town. He and Jean-Claude both want me for their own human servant. A war of the undead has begun. Over me. I would be flattered. If my life weren't at stake.

### THE LUNATIC CAFE

I thought I'd finally met the perfect guy—intelligent, attractive, and most important—still breathing. But every man has his faults, and Richard's—well, think full moon. Then think furry. Not only is Richard a werewolf, he is one of the top wolves in the local pack. And when some of them turn up missing, they come to me for help.

### BLOODY BONES

Bodies with missing pieces are upsetting at the best of times. When it looks like they've gotten that way because of a vampire serial killer—that's beyond upsetting. Add a creature right out of every child's nightmares to the mix, and it didn't take a degree in preternatural studies to figure out that something was very wrong in and around Branson, Missouri. And I was right in the middle of it.

### THE KILLING DANCE

The first hit man came after me at home, which should be against the rules. Then there was a second, and a third. Eventually, I found out that the word on the street was that Anita Blake, preternatural expert and vampire killer extraordinaire, was worth half a million dollars. Dead, not alive.

## BURNT OFFERINGS

I've always said you can't trust anyone who sleeps with the monsters.
But now I'm the one sharing a bed
with the Master Vampire of the City.
Me, Anita Blake. The woman the
vampires call the Executioner. Don't
ask. At any rate, it hits close to home
when an arsonist begins to target
vampire-owned businesses all over
town—an arsonist who seems to want
to destroy more than just property.

## BLUE MOON

You never forget your ex-fiancé.
Especially if he's an Alpha Werewolf.
So when I found out Richard, the
former love of my life, had gotten
himself thrown in jail for assaulting a
woman, I was off. Anita to the rescue.
Though Richard may be one of the
monsters, I knew he would never
harm a woman. And I've only got a
few days to spring Richard and find
out who framed him—and why.

## OBSIDIAN BUTTERFLY

Edward was a hit man. He specialized in monsters. Vampires, shape-shifters, anything and everything. He was an equal-opportunity killer. And I owed him a favor. One he was about to call in...

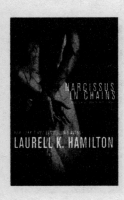

## NARCISSUS IN CHAINS

I'm still living this one. Read it and find out.

*from*

# GUILTY PLEASURES

**LAURELL K. HAMILTON**

Willie McCoy had been a jerk before he died. His being dead didn't change that. He sat across from me, wearing a loud plaid sport jacket. The polyester pants were primary Crayola green. His short, black hair was slicked back from a thin, triangular face. He had always reminded me of a bit player in a gangster movie. The kind that sells information, runs errands, and is expendable.

Of course now that Willie was a vampire, the expendable part didn't count anymore. But he was still selling information and running errands. No, death hadn't changed him much. But just in case, I avoided looking directly into his eyes. It was standard policy for dealing with vampires. He was a slime bucket, but now he was an undead slime bucket. It was a new category for me.

We sat in the quiet air-conditioned hush of my office. The powder blue walls, which Bert, my boss, thought would be soothing, made the room feel cold.

"Mind if I smoke?" he asked.

"Yes," I said, "I do."

"Damn, you aren't gonna make this easy, are you?"

I looked directly at him for a moment. His eyes were still brown. He caught me looking, and I looked down at my desk.

Willie laughed, a wheezing snicker of a sound. The laugh hadn't changed. "Geez, I love it. You're afraid of me."

"Not afraid, just cautious."

"You don't have to admit it. I can smell the fear on you, almost like somethin' touching my face, my brain. You're afraid of me, 'cause I'm a vampire."

I shrugged; what could I say? How do you lie to someone who can smell your fear? "Why are you here, Willie?"

"Geez, I wish I had a smoke." The skin began to jump at the corner of his mouth.

"I didn't think vampires had nervous twitches."

His hand went up, almost touched it. He smiled, flashing fangs. "Some things don't change."

I wanted to ask him, what does change? How does it feel to be dead? I knew other vampires, but Willie was the first I had known before and after death. It was a peculiar feeling. "What do you want?"

"Hey, I'm here to give you money. To become a client."

I glanced up at him, avoiding his eyes. His tie tack caught the overhead lights. Real gold. Willie had never had anything like that before. He was doing all right for a dead man. "I raise the dead for a living, no pun intended. Why would a vampire need a zombie raised?"

He shook his head, two quick jerks to either side. "No, no voodoo stuff. I wanna hire you to investigate some murderers."

"I am not a private investigator."

"But you got one of 'em on retainer to your outfit."

I nodded. "You could just hire Ms. Sims directly. You don't have to go through me for that."

Again that jerky head shake. "But she don't know about vampires the way you do."

I sighed. "Can we cut to the chase here, Willie? I have to leave"—I glanced at the wall clock—"in fifteen minutes. I don't like to leave a client waiting alone in a cemetery. They tend to get jumpy."

He laughed. I found the snickery laugh comforting, even with the fangs. Surely vampires should have rich, melodious laughs. "I'll bet they do. I'll just bet they do." His face sobered suddenly, as if a hand had wiped his laughter away.

I felt fear like a jerk in the pit of my stomach. Vampires could change movements like clicking a switch. If he could do that, what else could he do?

"You know about the vampires that are getting wasted over in the District?"

He made it a question, so I answered. "I'm familiar with them." Four vampires had been slaughtered in the new vampire club district. Their hearts had been torn out, their heads cut off.

"You still working with the cops?"

"I am still on retainer with the new task force."

He laughed again. "Yeah, the spook squad. Underbudgeted and undermanned, right."

"You've described most of the police work in this town."

"Maybe, but the cops feel like you do, Anita. What's one more dead vampire? New laws don't change that."

It had only been two years since Addison v. Clark. The court case gave us a revised version of what life was, and what death wasn't. Vampirism was legal in the good ol' U.S. of A. We were one of the few countries to acknowledge them. The immigration people were having fits trying to keep foreign vampires from immigrating in, well, flocks.

All sorts of questions were being fought out in court. Did heirs have to give back their inheritance? Were you widowed if your spouse became undead? Was it murder to slay a vampire? There was even a movement to give them the vote. Times were a-changing.

I stared at the vampire in front of me and shrugged. Did I really believe, what was one more dead vampire? Maybe. "If you believe I feel that way, why come to me at all?"

"Because you're the best at what you do. We need the best."

It was the first time he had said "we." "Who are you working for, Willie?"

He smiled then, a close secretive smile, like he knew something I should know. "Never you mind that. Money's real good. We want somebody who knows the night life to be looking into these murders."

"I've seen the bodies, Willie. I gave my opinions to the police."

"What'd you think?" He leaned forward in the chair, small hands flat on my desk. His fingernails were pale, almost white, bloodless.

"I gave a full report to the police." I stared up at him, almost looking him in the eye.

"Won't even give me that, will ya?"

"I am not at liberty to discuss police business with you."

"I told 'em you wouldn't go for this."

"Go for what? You haven't told me a damn thing."

"We want you to investigate the vampire killings, find out

who's, or what's, doing it. We'll pay you three times your normal fee."

I shook my head. That explained why Bert, the greedy son of a gun, had set up this meeting. He knew how I felt about vampires, but my contract forced me to at least meet with any client that had given Bert a retainer. My boss would do anything for money. Problem was he thought I should, too. Bert and I would be having a "talk" very soon.

I stood. "The police are looking into it. I am already giving them all the help I can. In a way I am already working on the case. Save your money."

He sat staring up at me, very still. It was not that lifeless immobility of the long dead, but it was a shadow of it.

Fear ran up my spine and into my throat. I fought an urge to draw my crucifix out of my shirt and drive him from my office. Somehow throwing a client out using a holy item seemed less than professional. So I just stood there, waiting for him to move.

"Why won't you help us?"

"I have clients to meet, Willie. I'm sorry that I can't help you."

"Won't help, you mean."

I nodded. "Have it your way." I walked around the desk to show him to the door.

He moved with a liquid quickness that Willie had never had, but I saw him move and was one step back from his reaching hand. "I'm not just another pretty face to fall for mind tricks."

"You saw me move."

"I heard you move. You're the new dead, Willie. Vampire or not, you've got a lot to learn."

He was frowning at me, hand still half-extended towards me. "Maybe, but no human could a stepped outta reach like that." He stepped up close to me, plaid jacket nearly brushing against me. Pressed together like that, we were nearly the same height—short. His eyes were on a perfect level with mine. I stared as hard as I could at his shoulder.

It took everything I had not to step back from him. But dammit, undead or not, he was Willie McCoy. I wasn't going to give him the satisfaction.

He said, "You ain't human, any more than I am."

I moved to open the door. I hadn't stepped away from him. I had stepped away to open the door. I tried convincing the sweat along my spine that there was difference. The cold feeling in my stomach wasn't fooled either.

"I really have to be going now. Thank you for thinking of Animators, Inc." I gave him my best professional smile, empty of meaning as a light bulb, but dazzling.

He paused in the open doorway. "Why won't you work for us? I gotta tell 'em something when I go back."

I wasn't sure, but there was something like fear in his voice. Would he get in trouble for failing? I felt sorry for him and knew it was stupid. He was the undead, for heaven's sake, but he stood looking at me, and he was still Willie, with his funny coats and small nervous hands.

"Tell them, whoever they are, that I don't work for vampires."

"A firm rule?" Again he made it sound like a question.

"Concrete."

There was a flash of something on his face, the old Willie peeking through. It was almost pity. "I wish you hadn't said that, Anita. These people don't like anybody telling 'em no."

"I think you've overstayed your welcome. I don't like to be threatened."

"It ain't a threat, Anita. It's the truth." He straightened his tie, fondling the new gold tie tack, squared his thin shoulders and walked out.

I closed the door behind him and leaned against it. My knees felt weak. But there wasn't time for me to sit here and shake. Mrs. Grundick was probably already at the cemetery. She would be standing there with her little black purse and her grown sons, waiting for me to raise her husband from the dead. There was a mystery of two very different wills. It was either years of court costs and arguments, or raise Albert Grundick from the dead and ask.

Everything I needed was in my car, even the chickens. I drew the silver crucifix free of my blouse and let it hang in full view. I have several guns, and I know how to use them. I keep a 9 mm Browning Hi-Power in my desk. The gun weighed a little over two pounds, silver-plated bullets and all. Silver won't kill a vampire, but it can discourage them. It forces them to have to heal the wounds, almost human slow. I wiped my sweaty palms on my skirt and went out.

Craig, our night secretary, was typing furiously at the computer keyboard. His eyes widened as I walked over the thick carpeting. Maybe it was the cross swinging on its long chain. Maybe it was the shoulder rig tight across my back, and the gun out in plain sight. He didn't mention either. Smart man.

I put my nice little corduroy jacket over it all. The jacket didn't lie flat over the gun, but that was okay. I doubted the Grundicks and their lawyers would notice.

I had gotten to see the sun rise as I drove home that morning. I hate sunrises. They mean I've overscheduled myself and worked all bloody night. St. Louis has more trees edging its highways than any other city I have driven through. I could almost admit the trees looked nice in the first light of dawn, almost. My apartment always looks depressingly white and cheerful in morning sunlight. The walls are the same vanilla ice cream white as every apartment I've ever seen. The carpeting is a nice shade of grey, preferable to that dog poop brown that is more common.

The apartment is a roomy one-bedroom. I am told it has a nice view of the park next door. You couldn't prove it by me. If I had my choice, there would be no windows. I get by with heavy drapes that turn the brightest day to cool twilight.

I switched the radio on low to drown the small noises of my day-living neighbors. Sleep sucked me under to the soft music of Chopin. A minute later the phone rang.

I lay there for a minute, cursing myself for forgetting to turn on the answering machine. Maybe if I ignored it? Five rings later I gave in. "Hello."

"Oh, I'm sorry. Did I wake you?"

It was a woman I didn't know. If it was a salesperson I was going to become violent. "Who is this?" I blinked at the bedside clock. It was eight. I'd had nearly two hours of sleep. Yippee.

"I'm Monica Vespucci." She said it like it should explain everything. It didn't.

"Yes." I tried to sound helpful, encouraging. I think it came out as a growl.

"Oh, my, uh. I'm the Monica that works with Catherine Maison."

I huddled around the receiver and tried to think. I don't think really well on two hours of sleep. Catherine was a good friend, a name I knew. She had probably mentioned this woman to me, but for the life of me, I couldn't place her. "Sure, Monica, yes. What do you want?" It sounded rude, even to me. "I'm sorry if I don't sound too good. I got off work at six."

"My god, you mean you've only had two hours of sleep. Do you want to shoot me, or what?"

I didn't answer the question. I'm not that rude. "Did you want something, Monica?"

"Sure, yes. I'm throwing a surprise bachelorette party for Catherine. You know she gets married next month."

I nodded, remembered she couldn't see me, and mumbled, "I'm in the wedding."

"Oh, sure, I knew that. Pretty dresses for the bridesmaids, don't you think?"

Actually, the last thing I wanted to spend a hundred and twenty dollars on was a long pink formal with puffy sleeves, but it was Catherine's wedding. "What about the bachelorette party?"

"Oh, I'm rambling, aren't I? And you just desperate for sleep."

I wondered if screaming at her would make her go away any faster. Naw, she'd probably cry. "What do you want, please, Monica?"

"Well, I know it's short notice, but everything just sort of slipped up on me. I meant to call you a week ago, but I just never got around to it."

This I believed. "Go on."

"The bachelorette party is tonight. Catherine says you don't drink, so I was wondering if you could be designated driver."

I just lay there for a minute, wondering how mad to get, and if it would do me any good. Maybe if I'd been more awake, I wouldn't have said what I was thinking. "Don't you think this is awfully short notice, since you want me to drive?"

"I know. I'm so sorry. I'm just so scattered lately. Catherine told me you usually have either Friday or Saturday night off. Is Friday not your night off this week?"

As a matter of fact it was, but I didn't really want to give up my only night off to this airhead on the other end of the phone. "I do have the night off."

"Great! I'll give you directions, and you can pick us up after work. Is that okay?"

It wasn't, but what else could I say. "That's fine."

"Pencil and paper?"

"You said you worked with Catherine, right?" I was actually beginning to remember Monica.

"Why, yes."

"I know where Catherine works. I don't need directions."

"Oh, how silly of me, of course. Then we'll see you about five. Dress up, but no heels. We may be dancing tonight."

I hate to dance. "Sure, see you then."

"See you tonight."

The phone went dead in my ear. I turned on the answering machine and cuddled back under the sheets. Monica worked with Catherine, that made her a lawyer. That was a frightening thought. Maybe she was one of those people who was only organized at work. Naw.

It occurred to me then, when it was too late, that I could just have refused the invitation. Damn. I was quick today. Oh, well, how bad could it be? Watching strangers get blitzed out of their minds. If I was lucky, maybe someone would throw up in my car.

I had the strangest dreams once I got back to sleep. All about this woman I didn't know, a coconut cream pie, and Willie McCoy's funeral.

Monica Vespucci was wearing a button that said, "Vampires are People, too." It was not a promising beginning to the evening. Her white blouse was silk with a high, flared collar framing a dark, health-club tan. Her hair was short and expertly cut; her makeup, perfect.

The button should have tipped me off to what kind of bachelorette party she'd planned. Some days I'm just slow to catch on.

I was wearing black jeans, knee-high boots, and a crimson blouse. My hair was made to order for the outfit, black curling just over the shoulders of the red blouse. The solid, nearly black-brown of my eyes matches the hair. Only the skin stands out, too pale, Germanic against the Latin darkness. A very ex-boyfriend once described me as a little china doll. He meant it as a compliment. I didn't take it that way. There are reasons why I don't date much.

The blouse was long-sleeved to hide the knife sheath on my right wrist and the scars on my left arm. I had left my gun locked in the trunk of my car. I didn't think the bachelorette party would get that out of hand.

"I'm so sorry that I put off planning this to the last minute, Catherine. That's why there's only three of us. Everybody else had plans," Monica said.

"Imagine that, people having plans for Friday night," I said.

Monica stared at me as if trying to decide whether I was joking or not.

Catherine gave me a warning glare. I gave them both my best angelic smile. Monica smiled back. Catherine wasn't fooled.

Monica began dancing down the sidewalk, happy as a

drunken clam. She had had only two drinks with dinner. It was a bad sign.

"Be nice," Catherine whispered.

"What did I say?"

"Anita." Her voice sounded like my father's used to sound when I'd stayed out too late.

I sighed. "You're just no fun tonight."

"I plan to be a lot of fun tonight." She stretched her arms skyward. She still wore the crumpled remains of her business suit. The wind blew her long, copper-colored hair. I've never been able to decide if Catherine would be prettier if she cut her hair, so you'd notice the face first, or if the hair was what made her pretty.

"If I have to give up one of my few free nights, then I am going to enjoy myself—immensely," she said.

There was a kind of fierceness to the last word. I stared up at her. "You are not planning to get falling-down drunk, are you?"

"Maybe." She looked smug.

Catherine knew I didn't approve of, or rather, didn't understand drinking. I didn't like having my inhibitions lowered. If I was going to cut loose, I wanted to be in control of just how loose I got.

We had left my car in a parking lot two blocks back. The one with the wrought-iron fence around it. There wasn't much parking down by the river. The narrow brick roads and ancient sidewalks had been designed for horses, not automobiles. The streets had been fresh-washed by a summer thunderstorm that had come and gone while we ate dinner. The first stars glittered overhead, like diamonds trapped in velvet.

Monica yelled, "Hurry up, slowpokes."

Catherine looked at me and grinned. The next thing I knew, she was running towards Monica.

"Oh, for heaven's sake," I muttered. Maybe if I'd had drinks with dinner, I'd have run, too, but I doubted it.

"Don't be an old stick in the mud," Catherine called back. Sticking the mud? I caught up to them walking. Monica was giggling. Somehow I had known she would be. Catherine and she were leaning against each other laughing. I suspected they might be laughing at me.

Monica calmed enough to fake an ominous stage whisper. "Do you know what lies around this corner?"

As a matter of fact, I did. The last vampire killing had been only four blocks from here. We were in what the vampires called "the District." Humans called it the Riverfront, or Blood Square, depending on if they were being rude or not.

"Guilty Pleasures," I said.

"Oh, pooh, you spoiled the surprise."

"What's Guilty Pleasures?" Catherine asked.

Monica giggled. "Oh, goodie, the surprise isn't spoiled after all." She put her arm through Catherine's. "You are going to love this, I promise you."

Maybe Catherine would; I knew I wouldn't, but I followed them around the corner anyway. The sign was a wonderful swirling neon the color of heart blood. The symbolism was not lost on me.

We went up three broad steps, and there was a vampire standing in front of the propped-open door. He had a black crew cut and small, pale eyes. His massive shoulders threatened to rip the tight black t-shirt he wore. Wasn't pumping iron redundant after you died?

Even standing on the threshold I could hear the busy hum of voices, laughter, music. That rich, murmurous sound of many people in a small space, determined to have a good time.

The vampire stood beside the door, very still. There was still a movement to him, an aliveness, for lack of a better term. He couldn't have been dead more than twenty years, if that. In the dark he looked almost human, even to me. He had fed already tonight. His skin was flushed and healthy. He looked damn near rosy-cheeked. A meal of fresh blood will do that to you.

Monica squeezed his arm. "Ooo, feel that muscle."

He grinned, flashing fangs. Catherine gasped. He grinned wider.

"Buzz here is an old friend, aren't you, Buzz?"

Buzz the vampire? Surely not.

But he nodded. "Go on in, Monica. Your table is waiting."

Table? What kind of clout did Monica have? Guilty Pleasures was one of the hottest clubs in the District, and they did not take reservations.

There was a large sign on the door. "No crosses, crucifixes, or other holy items allowed inside." I read the sign and walked past it. I had no intention of getting rid of my cross.

A rich, melodious voice floated around us. "Anita, how good of you to come."

The voice belonged to Jean-Claude, club owner and master vampire. He looked like a vampire was supposed to look. Softly curling hair tangled with the high white lace of an antique shirt. Lace spilled over pale, long-fingered hands. The shirt hung open, giving a glimpse of lean bare chest framed by more frothy lace. Most men couldn't have worn a shirt like that. The vampire made it seem utterly masculine.

"You two know each other?" Monica sounded surprised.

"Oh, yes," Jean-Claude said. "Ms. Blake and I have met before."

"I've been helping the police work cases on the Riverfront."

"She is their vampire expert." He made the last word soft and warm and vaguely obscene.

Monica giggled. Catherine was staring at Jean-Claude, eyes wide and innocent. I touched her arm, and she jerked as if waking from a dream. I didn't bother to whisper because I knew he would have heard me anyway. "Important safety tip—never look a vampire in the eye."

She nodded. The first hint of fear showed in her face.

"I would never harm such a lovely young woman." He took Catherine's hand and raised it to his mouth. A mere brush of lips. Catherine blushed.

He kissed Monica's hand as well. He looked at me and laughed. "Do not worry, my little animator. I will not touch you. That would be cheating."

He moved to stand next to me. I stared fixedly at his chest.
There was a burn scar almost hidden in the lace. The burn
was in the shape of a cross. How many decades ago had someone shoved a cross into his flesh?

"Just as you having a cross would be an unfair advantage."

What could I say? In a way he was right.

It was a shame that it wasn't merely the shape of a cross
that hurt a vampire. Jean-Claude would have been in deep shit.
Unfortunately, the cross had to be blessed, and backed up by
faith. An atheist waving a cross at a vampire was a truly pitiful sight.

He breathed my name like a whisper against my skin.
"Anita, what are you thinking?"

The voice was so damn soothing. I wanted to look up and
see what face went with such words. Jean-Claude had been
intrigued by my partial immunity to him. That and the cross-
shaped burn scar on my arm. He found the scar amusing. Every
time we met, he did his best to bespell me, and I did my best to
ignore him. I had won up until now.

"You never objected to me carrying a cross before."

"You were on police business then; now you are not."

I stared at his chest and wondered if the lace was as soft
as it looked; probably not.

"Are you so insecure in your own powers, little animator? Do you believe that all your resistance to me resides in that
piece of silver around your neck?"

I didn't believe that, but I knew it helped. Jean-Claude was
a self-admitted two hundred and five years old. A vampire gains
a lot of power in two centuries. He was suggesting I was a cow-
ard. I was not.

I reached up to unfasten the chain. He stepped away from
me and turned his back. The cross spilled silver into my hands.
A blonde human woman appeared beside me. She handed me
a check stub and took the cross. Nice, a holy item check girl.

I felt suddenly underdressed without my cross. I slept and
showered in it.

Jean-Claude stepped close again. "You will not resist the

show tonight, Anita. Someone will enthrall you."

"No," I said. But it's hard to be tough when you're staring at someone's chest. You really need eye contact to play tough, but that was a no-no.

He laughed. The sound seemed to rub over my skin, like the brush of fur. Warm and feeling ever so slightly of death.

Monica grabbed my arm. "You're going to love this, I promise you."

"Yes," Jean-Claude said. "It will be a night you will never forget."

"Is that a threat?"

He laughed again, that warm awful sound. "This is a place of pleasure, Anita, not violence."

Monica was pulling at my arm. "Hurry, the entertainment's about to begin."

"Entertainment?" Catherine asked.

I had to smile. "Welcome to the world's only vampire strip club, Catherine."

"You are joking."

"Scout's honor." I glanced back at the door; I don't know why. Jean-Claude stood utterly still, no sense of anything, as if he were not there at all. Then he moved, one pale hand raised to his lips. He blew me a kiss across the room. The night's entertainment had begun.

*from*

# THE LUNATIC CAFE

LAURELL K. HAMILTON

**G**uilty Pleasures is in the heart of the vampire district. Its glowing neon sign bled into the night sky, giving the blackness a crimson tint like a distant house fire. I hadn't come to the district unarmed after dark for a very long time. Okay, I had the knife, and it was better than arm wrestling, but against a vampire, not much better.

Stephen was beside me. A werewolf wasn't a bad bodyguard, but somehow Stephen didn't look scary enough. He was only an inch or two taller than me, slender as a willow with just enough shoulder definition to make him look masculine. To say his pants were tight wasn't enough. They were leather and looked painted on like a second skin. It was hard not to notice that his derriere was tight and firm. The leather jacket cut him off at the waist, so the view was unobstructed.

I was wearing my black trench coat again. It had a little bit of blood on it, but if I cleaned it, it would be wet. Wet would not keep me warm. My sweater, one of my favorite sweaters, was torn off one shoulder down to the line of my bra. Too cold without a coat. Gretchen owed me a sweater. Maybe after I got my guns back, we'd talk about that.

Three broad steps led up to closed doors. Buzz the Vampire was guarding them. It was the worst vampire name I'd ever heard. It wasn't great if you were human, but Buzz seemed all wrong for a vampire. It was a great name for a bouncer. He was tall and muscle-bound with a black crew cut. He seemed to be wearing the same black T-shirt he'd worn in July.

I knew vampires couldn't freeze to death, but I hadn't known they didn't get cold. Most vampires tried to play human. They wore coats in the winter. Maybe they didn't need them the same way Gretchen hadn't needed to take the knife from her throat. Maybe it was all pretend.

He smiled, flashing fangs. My reaction seemed to disappoint him. "You missed a set, Stephen. The boss is pissed."

Stephen sort of shrank in on himself. Buzz seemed to get larger, pleased with himself. "Stephen was helping me. I don't think Jean-Claude will mind."

Buzz squinted at me, really seeing my face for the first

time. "Shit, what happened to you?"

"If Jean-Claude wants you to know, he'll tell you," I said. I walked past him. There was a large sign on the door: No Crosses, Crucifixes, or Other Holy Items Allowed Inside. I pushed the doors open and kept walking, my cross securely around my neck. They could pry it from my cold dead hands if they wanted it tonight.

Stephen stayed at my heels, almost as if he were afraid of Buzz. Buzz wasn't that old a vampire, less than twenty years. He still had a sense of "aliveness" to him. That utter stillness that the old ones have hadn't touched the bouncer yet. So why was a werewolf afraid of a new vampire? Good question.

It was Sunday night and the place was packed. Didn't any-one have work tomorrow? The noise washed over us like a wave of nearly solid ground. That rich murmurous sound of many people in a small space determined to have a good time. The lights were as bright as they ever got. The small stage empty. We were between shows.

A blond woman greeted us at the door. "Do you have any holy items to declare?" She smiled when she said it. The holy-item check girl.

I smiled when I said, "Nope."

She didn't question me, just smiled and walked away. A male voice said, "Just a moment, Sheila." The tall vampire that strode towards us was lovely to look at. He had high sculpted cheekbones and short blond hair styled to perfection. He was too masculine to be beautiful, and too perfect to be real. Robert had been a stripper last time I was here. It looked as though he'd moved up into management.

Sheila waited, looking from Robert to me. "She lied to me?"

Robert nodded. "Hello, Anita."

"Hello. Are you the manager here now?"

He nodded.

I didn't like it, him being manager. He'd failed me once, or rather failed Jean-Claude's orders. Failed to keep someone safe. That someone had died. Robert hadn't even gotten bloody trying to stop the monsters. He should at least have gotten hurt trying. I didn't insist he die to keep people safe, but he should have tried harder. I'd never completely trust him or forgive him.

"You are wearing a holy item, Anita. Unless on police business, you must give it to Sheila."

I glanced up at him. His eyes were blue. I glanced down, then up, and realized I could meet his eyes. He was over a hundred years old, not nearly as powerful as Gretchen, but I shouldn't have been able to meet his eyes.

His eyes widened. "You have to give it up. Those are the rules."

Maybe being able to look him in the eyes had given me courage, or maybe I had had enough for one night. "Is Gretchen here?"

He looked surprised. "Yes, she's in the back room with Jean-Claude."

"Then you can't have the cross."

"I can't let you in then. Jean-Claude is very clear on that." There was a hint of unease in his voice, almost fear. Good.

"Take a good look at my face, Bobby-boy. Gretchen did it. If she's here, I keep the cross."

Frown lines formed between his perfect brows. "Jean-Claude said no exceptions." He stepped closer, and I let him. He lowered his voice as much as he could and be heard above the noise. "He said if I ever fail him again in anything large or small, he'll punish me."

Normally, I thought statements like that were pitiful or cruel. I agreed with this one.

"Go ask Jean-Claude," I said.

He shook his head. "I cannot trust you to stay here. If you get past me with the cross, I will have failed."

This was getting tiresome. "Can Stephen go ask?"

Robert nodded.

Stephen sort of hung by me. He hadn't recovered from Buzz's remarks. "Is Jean-Claude mad at me for missing my set?"

"You should have called if you couldn't make your set,"

Robert said. "I had to go on in your place."

"Good to be useful," I said.

Robert frowned at me. "Stephen should have called."

"He was taking me to a doctor. You got a problem with that?"

"Jean-Claude may."

"Then bring the great man out and let's ask him. I'm tired of standing in the door."

"Anita, how good of you to grace us with your presence." Gretchen was practically purring with anticipation.

"Robert won't let me pass."

She turned her eyes to the vampire. He took a step back. She hadn't even unleashed any of that impressive magic yet. Robert scared easy for a century-old corpse.

"We have been awaiting her, Robert. Jean-Claude is most anxious to see her."

He swallowed hard. "I was told that no one came inside with a holy item other than the police. No exceptions were to be made."

"Not even for the master's sweetheart." She put a lot of irony in that last part.

Robert either didn't get it or ignored it. "Until Jean-Claude tells me differently, she doesn't go through with a cross."

Gretchen stalked around us all. I wasn't sure who looked more worried. "Take off the little cross and let us get this over with."

I shook my head. "Nope."

"It didn't do you a lot of good earlier tonight," she said.

She had a point. For the first time I realized I hadn't even thought of bringing out my cross earlier. I'd gone for my weapons, but not my faith. Pretty damn sad.

I fingered the cool silver of the chain. "The cross stays."

"You are both spoiling my fun," she said. The way she said it made that sound like a very bad thing. "I'll give you one of your weapons back."

A moment before I'd have agreed, but not now. I was embarrassed that I had not gone for my cross earlier. It wouldn't have kept her from jumping me at the beginning. She was too powerful for that. But it might have chased her off Louie. I was going to have to stop skipping church even if I didn't get to sleep at all.

"No."

"Is this your way of getting out of our bargain?" Her voice was low and warm with the first stirrings of anger.

"I keep my word," I said.

"I will escort her through, Robert." She raised a hand to stop his complaining. "If Jean-Claude blames you, tell him I was going to tear your throat out." She stepped into him until only a breath separated their bodies. It was only standing that close that you realized that Robert was taller by a head and a half. Gretchen seemed bigger than that. "It isn't a lie, Robert. I think you're weak, a liability. I would kill you now if our master did not need us both. If you still fear Jean-Claude, remember that he wants you alive. I do not."

Robert swallowed hard enough that it had to hurt. He didn't back up. Brownie point for him. She moved that fraction closer, and he jumped back as if he'd been shot. "Fine, fine, take her through."

Gretchen's lip curled in disgust. One thing we agreed on: we didn't like Robert. If we had one thing in common, maybe there'd be more. Maybe we could be girlfriends. Yeah, right.

The noise level had dropped to a background murmur. We had everybody's attention. Nothing like a floor show. "Is there supposed to be an act on stage right now?" I asked.

Robert nodded. "Yes, I need to introduce him."

"Go do your job, Robert." The words were thick with scorn. Gretchen gave good scorn.

Robert left us, obviously relieved. "Wimp," I said softly.

"Come, Anita, Jean-Claude is waiting for us." She stalked away, long pale coat swinging out behind her. Stephen and I exchanged glances. He shrugged. I followed her, and he trailed behind as if he were afraid of losing me.

Jean-Claude's office was like being inside a domino. Stark white walls, white carpet, black lacquer desk, black office chair, black leather couch against one wall, and two straight-backed chairs sat in front of the desk. The desk and chairs were Oriental, set with enamel pictures of cranes and Oriental women in flowing robes. I'd always liked the desk, not that I would admit it out loud.

There was a black lacquer screen in one corner. I'd never seen it before. It was large, hiding one entire corner. A dragon curled across the screen in oranges and reds, with huge bulbous eyes. It was a nice addition to the room. It was not a comfortable room, but it was stylish. Like Jean-Claude.

He sat on the leather couch dressed all in black. The shirt had a high, stiff collar that framed his face. It was hard to tell where his hair left off and the shirt began. The collar was pinned at his throat, with a thumb-size ruby pendant. The shirt was open down to his belt, leaving a triangle of pale, pale skin showing. Only the pendant kept the shirt from opening completely.

The cuffs were as wide and stiff as the collar, nearly hiding his hands. He raised one hand, and I could see the cuffs were open on one side so he could still use his hands. Black jeans and velvet black boots completed the outfit.

I'd seen the pendant before, but the shirt was certainly new. "Spiffy," I said.

He smiled. "Do you like it?" He straightened the cuffs, as if they needed it.

"It's a nice change from white," I said.

"Stephen, we were expecting you earlier." His voice was mild enough, but there was an undertaste of something dark and unpleasant.

"Stephen took me to the doctor."

His midnight blue eyes turned back to me. "Is your latest police investigation getting rough?"

"No," I said. I glanced at Gretchen. She was looking at Jean-Claude.

"Tell him," she said.

I didn't think she was referring to my accusing her of trying to kill me. It was time for a little honesty, or at least a little drama. I was sure Jean-Claude wouldn't disappoint us.

"Stephen needs to leave now," I said. I didn't want him getting killed trying to protect me. He wasn't up to being anything but cannon fodder. Not against Jean-Claude.

"Why?" he asked. He sounded suspicious.

"Get on with it," Gretchen said.

I shook my head. "Stephen doesn't need to be here."

"Get out, Stephen," Jean-Claude said. "I am not angry with you for missing your set. Anita is more important to me than your being on time to your job."

That was nice to know.

Stephen gave a sort of bob, almost a bow to Jean-Claude, flashed a look at me, and hesitated. "Go on, Stephen. I'll be all right."

I didn't have to reassure him twice. He fled.

"What have you been up to, *ma petite?*"

I glanced at Gretchen. She had eyes only for him. Her face looked hungry, as if she'd waited for this a long time. I stared into his dark blue eyes and realized that I could without vampire marks; I could meet his eyes.

Jean-Claude noticed it, too. His eyes widened just a bit. "*Ma petite*, you are full of surprises tonight."

"You ain't seen nothing yet," I said.

"By all means, continue. I do love a surprise."

I doubted he'd like this one. I took a deep breath and said it fast, as if that would make it go down better, like a spoonful of sugar. "Richard asked me to marry him, and I said yes." I could have added, "But I'm not sure anymore," but I didn't. I was too confused to offer up anything but the bare facts. If he tried to kill me, maybe I'd add details. Until then . . . we'd wait it out.

Jean-Claude just sat there. He didn't move at all. The heater clicked on, and I jumped. The vent was above the couch. The air played along his hair, the cloth of his shirt, but it was like watching a mannequin. The hair and clothes worked but the rest was stone.

The silence stretched and filled the room. The heater died, and the quiet was so profound I could hear the blood rushing in my ears. It was like the stillness before creation. You knew something big was coming. You just didn't know quite what. I let the silence flow around me. I wouldn't be the one to break it, because I was afraid of what came next. This utter calmness was more unnerving than anger would have been. I didn't know what to do with it, so I did nothing. A course of action I seldom regret.

It was Gretchen who broke first. "Did you hear her, Jean-Claude? She is to wed another. She loves another."

He blinked once, a long, graceful sweep of lashes. "Ask her now if she loves me, Gretchen."

Gretchen stepped in front of me, blocking Jean-Claude from view. "What does it matter? She's going to marry someone else."

"Ask her." It was a command.

Gretchen whirled to face me. The bones in her face stood out under the skin, lips thin with rage. "You don't love him."

It wasn't exactly a question, so I didn't answer it. Jean-Claude's voice came lazy and full of some dark meaning that I didn't understand. "Do you love me, *ma petite*?"

I stared into Gretchen's rage-filled face and said, "I don't suppose you'd believe me if I said no?"

"Can you not simply say yes?"

"Yes, in some dark, twisted part of my soul, I love you. Happy?"

He smiled. "How can you marry him if you love me?"

"I love him, too, Jean-Claude."

"In the same way?"

"No," I said.

"How do you love us differently?"

The questions were getting trickier. "How am I supposed to explain something to you that I don't even understand myself?"

"Try."

"You're like great Shakespearean tragedy. If Romeo and Juliet hadn't committed suicide, they'd have hated each other in a year. Passion is a form of love, but it isn't real. It doesn't last."

"And how do you feel about Richard?" His voice was full of some strange emotion. It should have been anger, but it felt different from that. Almost as if it were an emotion I didn't have a word for.

"I don't just love Richard, I like him. I enjoy his company. I . . ." I hated explaining myself. "Oh, hell, Jean-Claude, I can't put it into words. I can see spending my life with Richard, and I can't see it with you."

"Have you set a date?"

"No," I said.

He cocked his head to one side, studying me. "It is the truth but there is some bit of lie to it. What are you holding back, *ma petite*?"

I frowned at him. "I've told you the truth."

"But not all of it."

I didn't want to tell him. He'd enjoy it too much. I felt vaguely disloyal to Richard. "I'm not completely sure about marrying Richard."

"Why not?" There was something in his face that was almost hopeful. I couldn't let him get the wrong idea.

"I saw him go all spooky. I felt his . . . power."

"And?"

"And now I'm not sure," I said.

"He's not human enough for you, either." He threw back his head and laughed. A joyous outpouring of sound that coated me like chocolate. Heavy and sweet and annoying.

"She loves another," Gretchen said. "Does it matter if she doubts him? She doubts you. She rejects you, Jean-Claude. Isn't that enough?"

"Did you do all that to her face?"

She stalked a tight circle like a tiger in a cage. "She does not love you as I do." She knelt in front of him, hands touching his legs, face staring up into his. "Please, I love you. I've always loved you. Kill her or let her marry this man. She doesn't deserve your adoration."

He ignored her. "Are you all right, *ma petite*?"

"I'm fine."

Gretchen dug fingers into his jeans, grabbing at him. "Please, please!"

I didn't like her, but the pain, the hopeless pain in her voice was horrible to hear. She'd tried to kill me, and I still felt sorry for her.

"Leave us, Gretchen."

"No!" She clutched at him.

"I forbade you to harm her. You disobeyed me. I should kill you."

She just stayed kneeling, gazing up at him. I couldn't see her expression and was glad of it. I wasn't big on adoration. "Jean-Claude, please, please, I only did it for you. She doesn't love you."

His hand was suddenly around her neck. I hadn't seen him move. It was magic. Whatever was letting me look him in the eyes, it didn't stop him playing with my mind. Or maybe he was just that fast. Naw.

She tried to talk. His fingers closed, and the words came out as small, choked sounds. He stood, drawing her to her feet. Her hands wrapped around his wrist, trying to keep him from hanging her. He kept lifting until her feet dangled in the air. I knew she could fight him. I'd felt the strength in those delicate-seeming hands. Except for her hand on his wrist she didn't even struggle. Would she let him kill her? Would he do it? Could I stand here and just watch?

He stood there in his wonderful black shirt, looking elegant and scrumptious, and holding Gretchen with one arm, straight up. He walked towards his desk still holding her. He kept his balance effortlessly. Even a lycanthrope couldn't have done it, not like that. I watched his slender body walk across the carpet and knew he could pretend all he wanted to, but it wasn't human. He wasn't human.

He set her feet on the carpet on the far side of the desk. He relaxed his grip on her throat but didn't let her go.

"Jean-Claude, please. Who is she that the Master of the City should beg for her attention?"

He kept his hand resting on her throat, not squeezing now.

He pushed the screen back with his free hand. It folded back to reveal a coffin. It sat up off the ground on a cloth-draped pedestal. The wood was nearly black and polished to a mirrorlike shine.

Gretchen's eyes widened. "Jean-Claude, Jean-Claude, I'm sorry. I didn't kill her. I could have. Ask her. I could have killed her, but I didn't. Ask her. Ask her!" Her voice was pure panic.

"Anita." That one word slithered across my skin, thick and full of foreboding. I was very glad that that voice was not angry with me.

"She could have killed me with the first rush," I said.

"Why do you think she did not do it?"

"I think she got distracted trying to draw it out. To enjoy it more."

"No, no, I was just threatening her. Trying to frighten her away. I knew you wouldn't want me to kill her. I knew that, or she'd be dead."

"You were always a bad liar, Gretel."

Gretel?

He raised the lid on the coffin with one hand, drawing her nearer to it.

She jerked away from him. His fingernails drew bloody furrows on her throat. She stood behind the office chair, putting it between her and him, as if it would help. Blood trickled down her throat.

"Do not make me force you, Gretel."

"My name is Gretchen and has been for over a hundred years." It was the first real spirit I'd seen in her against Jean-Claude anyway. I fought the urge to applaud. It wasn't hard.

"You were Gretel when I found you, and you are Gretel still. Do not force me to remind you of what you are, Gretel."

"I will not go into that cursed box willingly. I won't do it."

"Do you really want Anita to see you at your worst?"

I thought I already had.

"I will not go." Her voice was firm, not confident, but stubborn. She meant it.

Jean-Claude stood very still. He raised one hand in a languid gesture. There was no other word for it. The movement was almost dancelike.

Gretchen staggered, grabbing at the chair for support. Her face seemed to have shrunk. It wasn't the drawing down of power that I had seen on her earlier. Not the ethereal corpse that would tear your throat out and dance in the blood. The flesh squeezed down, wrapping tight on the bones. She was withering. Not aging, dying.

She opened her mouth and screamed.

"My God, what's happening to her?"

Gretchen stood clutching bird-thin hands on the chair back. She looked like a mummified corpse. Her bright lipstick was a gruesome slash across her face. Even her yellow hair had thinned, dry and brittle as straw.

Jean-Claude walked towards her, still graceful, still lovely, still monstrous. "I gave you eternal life, and I can take it back, never forget that."

She made a low mewling sound in her throat. She held out one feeble hand to him, beseeching.

"Into the box," he said. His voice made that last word dark and terrible, as if he'd said "hell" and meant it.

He had beaten the fight out of her, or maybe stolen was the word. I'd never seen anything like this. A new vampire power that I'd never even heard whispered in folklore. Shit.

Gretchen took a trembling step towards the coffin. Two painful, dragging steps and she lost her grip on the chair. She fell, bone-thin arms catching her full weight, the way you're not supposed to. A good way to get your arm broken. Gretchen didn't seem to be worried about broken bones. Couldn't blame her.

She knelt on the floor, head hanging as if she didn't have the strength to rise. Jean-Claude just stood there, staring at her. He made no move to help her. If it had been anyone but Gretchen, I might have helped her myself.

I must have made some movement towards her because Jean-Claude made a back-away gesture to me. "If she fed on a human at this moment, all her strength would return. She is very frightened. I would not tempt her right now, *ma petite*."

I stayed where I was. I hadn't planned on helping her, but I didn't like watching it.

"Crawl," he said.

She started to crawl.

I'd had enough. "You've made your point, Jean-Claude. If you want her in the coffin, just pick her up and put her there."

He looked at me. There was something almost amused in his face. "You feel pity for her, *ma petite*. She meant to kill you. You know that."

"I'd have no problem shooting her, but this . . ." I didn't have a word for it. He wasn't just humiliating her. He was stripping her of herself. I shook my head. "You're tormenting her. If it's for my benefit, I've seen enough. If it's for your benefit, then stop it."

"It is for her benefit, *ma petite*. She has forgotten who her master is. A month or two in a coffin will remind her of that."

Gretchen had reached the foot of the pedestal. She had grabbed handfuls of the cloth but couldn't drag herself to her feet.

"I think she's been reminded enough."

"You are so harsh, *ma petite*, so pragmatic, yet suddenly something will move you to pity. And your pity is as strong as your hate."

"But not nearly as fun," I said.

He smiled and lifted the lid of the coffin. The inside was white silk, of course. He knelt and lifted Gretchen. Her limbs lay awkwardly in his arms as if they didn't quite work. As he lifted her over the lip of the coffin, her long coat dragged against the wood. Something in her pocket clunked, solid and heavy.

I almost hated to ask—almost. "If that's my gun in her pocket, I need it back."

He laid her almost gently in the silk lining, then rifled her pockets. He held the Browning in one hand and began to lower the lid. Her skeletal hands raised, trying to stop its descent.

Watching those thin hands beat at the air, I almost let it go.

"There should be another gun and a knife."

He widened his eyes at me, but nodded. He held the Browning out to me. I walked forward and took it. I was standing close enough to see her eyes. They were pale and cloudy, like the eyes of the very old, but there was enough expression left for terror.

Her eyes rolled wildly, staring at me. There was a mute appeal in that look. Desperation was too mild a word for it. She looked at me, not Jean-Claude, as if she knew that I was the only person in the room that gave a damn. If it bothered Jean-Claude, you couldn't tell it by his face.

I tucked the Browning under my arm. It felt good to have it back. He held the Firestar out to me. "I cannot find the knife. If you want to search her yourself, feel free."

I stared down at the dry, wrinkled skin, the lipless face. Her neck was as skinny as a chicken's. I shook my head. "I don't want it that bad."

He laughed, and even now the sound curled along my skin like velvet. A joyous sociopath.

He closed the lid, and she made horrible sounds, as though she were trying to scream and had no voice to do it with. Her thin hands beat against the lid.

Jean-Claude snapped the locks in place and leaned over the closed coffin. He whispered, "Sleep." Almost immediately the sounds slowed. He repeated the word once more, and the sounds ceased.

"How did you do that?"

"Quiet her?"

I shook my head. "All of it."

"I am her master."

"No, Nikolaos was your master, but she couldn't do that. She'd have done it to you if she could have."

"Perceptive of you, and very true. I made Gretchen. Nikolaos did not make me. Being the master vampire that brings someone over gives you certain powers over them. As you saw."

"Nikolaos had made most of the vampires in her little entourage, right?"

He nodded.

"If she could have done what you just did, I'd have seen it. She'd have shown it off."

He gave a small smile. "Again perceptive. There are a variety of powers that a master vampire can possess. Calling an animal, levitation, resistance to silver."

"Is that why my knife didn't seem to hurt Gretchen?"

"Yes."

"But each master has a different arsenal of gifts."

"Arsenal, it is an appropriate word. Now, where were we, *ma petite*? Ah, yes, I could kill Richard."

Here we go again.

*from*

# OBSIDIAN BUTTERFLY

**LAURELL K. HAMILTON**

Obsidian Butterfly, the club, was located between Santa Fe and Albuquerque. The club was set back from the road like one of the Indian casinos. It had high-class tourist trap written all over it. The parking lot was so full we had to circle to find a spot.

The building was done in faux-Aztec temple. Or for all I knew real Aztec temple. But the outside of the building looked like a movie set. Red neon traced square carved faces, and the name was traced in more red neon. There was a line stretching around the corner of the building and out into the hot summer dark. This was not my town. I didn't know the manager, so I couldn't jump the line. I also did not want to stand in the line.

Edward walked up the line, confident, as if he knew something I didn't. We followed him like obedient puppies. We weren't the only foursome trying to get into the club. We were the only foursome that wasn't made up of couples. To blend in we needed at least one more woman. But Edward didn't seem to be trying to blend in. He walked up to the head of the line where a large, broad-shouldered man of very Indian descent stood bare-chested, wearing what looked like a skirt but probably wasn't, and a heavy faux-gold collar that covered most of his shoulders like a mantle. He was wearing a crown covered in macaw feathers and other smaller feathers that I couldn't identify.

If this was just the bouncer at the door, I was actually interested in seeing the show. Though I hoped they had access to lots and lots of pet parrots and hadn't actually slaughtered birds just for the outfits.

"We're Professor Dallas's party. She's expecting us," Edward said in his best hail-fellow-well-met voice.

The feather and gold bedecked man said, "Names." He uncrossed his arms and looked at a clipboard that had been in his hand the entire time.

"Ted Forrester, Bernardo Spotted-Horse, Olaf Gundersson and Anita Lee." The new last name stopped me. Apparently, he was serious about me going in incognito.

"IDs."

I tried very hard to keep my face blank, but it was an effort. I didn't have any fake ID. I looked at Edward.

He handed his driver's license to the man, then still smiling, said, "And now aren't you glad that I didn't let you leave your license in the car." He handed a second license to the man.

He looked at both for longer than I thought he should have, as if he suspected something. My shoulders were actually tight, waiting for him to turn to me and say, ah-hah, fake ID, but he didn't. He handed both licenses back to Edward, and turned to Bernardo and Olaf. They waited with their licenses out, as if they'd done this before.

Edward moved back to stand by me and handed me the license. I took it and looked at it. It was a New Mexico license with an address on it that I didn't know. But it was my picture, and it said Anita Lee. The height, weight, and the rest were accurate, just the name and address were wrong.

"Better put it in your pocket. I may not be around to find it next time," he said.

I slipped it in my pocket along with my other license, a lipstick, and some money, and an extra cross. I wasn't sure whether to be flattered or insulted that Edward had set up a secret identity for me. Of course, maybe it was just the license, but knowing Edward there'd be more to it. There usually was.

The big double doors were opened by another large muscled guy in a skirt, though he didn't have a feather crown or a nifty collar. A lesser bouncer, apparently. The doors led into a darkened room thick with an incense I didn't recognize. The walls were completely covered with heavy drapes, only another set of double doors showing the way.

Another bouncer, this one blond and tanned the color of thick honey, opened the door. He had feathers woven into his short hair. He winked at me as we went through the door, but it was Bernardo he watched the closest. Maybe he was looking for weapons, but I think he was watching Bernardo's butt. He wouldn't see a weapon from the back. Bernardo had transferred his gun to a front cross draw because the gun had showed a lump at the back. Which told you how snug the pants fit in back.

The room we entered was large, stretching out and out into the near darkness. People sat at square stone tables that looked suspiciously like altars to me. Or at least what Hollywood is always using for altars. The "stage" took up most of the far left wall, but it wasn't a stage, not really. It was being used as a stage, but it was a temple. It was as if someone had sliced off the top of a pyramid temple and transported it here to this night club, in a city so far removed from the lush jungles where the building began that the stones themselves must be lonely.

A woman appeared in front of Edward. She looked as ethnic as the first doorman with high sculpted cheekbones, and a fall of shiny black hair that fell to her knees as she moved through the tables. She had menus in her dark hands, so I assumed she was the hostess. But her dress was red with a black design, and I knew silk when I saw it. The dress was vaguely oriental and didn't match the decor of the room, or the waitresses hurrying to and fro in odd loose dresses made of some rough material. The waitresses struggled along in loose-fitting sandals, while the hostess glided before us in high heels the same scarlet as her dress and perfectly manicured nails.

She was beautiful in a tall, slender, graceful fashion, like a model, but she was a discordant note, as if she belonged to a different theme. She showed us to a table that was in the very front with a view dead center of the temple. There was a woman at the table, who stood and offered us her hand as we sat down. Her handshake was firm, and her hand was about my size. It takes practice to have a firm handshake with hands this small.

Professor Dallas, call me Dallas, was shorter than I was, and so petite that in the right clothes she'd have looked prepubescent. She wore tan Docker pants, a white polo shirt, with a tweed jacket complete with leather elbow patches, as if she'd read the dress code for college professors and was trying to conform. Her hair was shoulder length, a baby fine, medium brown. Her face was small and triangular and as pale and perfect as God had intended it to be. Her glasses were gold wire frames and too large for the small face. If this was her idea of party clothes, someone needed to take her shopping. But somehow I didn't think the good doctor gave a shit. I like that in a woman.

A man stepped out of the odd-shaped door at the top of the temple. The moment he stepped out, silence fell in rings around him, spreading out and out into the murmuring audience until it was so quiet I could hear the pulse of my own blood. I'd never heard a crowd this large go so quiet so quickly. I'd have said it was magic, but it wasn't, not exactly. But this man's presence was a sort of magic. He could have worn jeans and a T-shirt and he'd still have commanded your attention. Of course, what he was wearing was pretty eye-catching all on its own.

His crown was a mass of thin, long feathers, a strange greenish, bluish, goldish color, so that as he moved they shifted color like a trapped greenish rainbow hovering in a fan of colors above his forehead. His cape hung nearly to his knees and seemed to be formed of the same feathers as his headdress, so that he moved in a wave of iridescence. The body that showed was strong, square, and dark. I was sitting close enough to tell if he was handsome or not, but staring at him, I wasn't sure. It was impossible to separate his face from that presence, and so the face didn't matter much. He was attractive, not because of the length of a nose or the turn of a chin, but just because.

I found myself sitting up a little straighter in my seat, as if coming to attention. The moment I did it, I knew that even if it wasn't magic, it was something. I had to fight to tear my gaze from him and look at the others at the table.

Bernardo was gazing at him, as was Doctor Dallas. Edward was gazing out over the hushed crowd. Olaf was studying the doctor. He watched her, not as a man watches a woman, but as a cat watches a bird through cage bars. If Dallas noticed, she ignored it, but somehow I think she didn't notice. I think even with the man's presence filling the room, his rich voice riding the air, I'd have felt Olaf's gaze like a cold wind down my spine. That Dallas was oblivious to it made me worry about her, just a little, and made me very sure that I never wanted Olaf alone with her. Her survival instincts just weren't up to it.

The man, king or high priest, talked in rich tones. I caught part of it. Something about the month of Toxcatal, and a chosen one. I could not concentrate on his voice, any more than I could gaze upon him because to give him too much of my attention meant I was caught up in the spell he was weaving over the crowd. It wasn't a spell in the true sense of the word, but there was power in it, if not magic. The difference between magic and power can be very small. I'd been forced to accept that fact in the last two years.

The high priest was human, but there was a taste of ages to him. There are just not that many ways for a human to last centuries. One way is to be the human servant of a powerful master vamp. Unless Obsidian Butterfly was more generous about sharing her power than most of the Masters of the City that I'd met, the high priest belonged to her. He was too powerful an echo of his master to be endured unless she was that master. Master vamps have a tendency to either destroy or own that which is powerful.

The high priest had been powerful in life, a charismatic leader. Now centuries of practice had turned that charisma into a kind of magic. I'd had full-fledged vamps not affect me this much. If this was the servant, how scary was the master going to be? I sat there at the stone table, flexing my shoulders to feel the tightness of the shoulder holster. I was glad I'd packed an extra clip of bullets. I moved my wrists just enough to feel the knives resting against my arms. I was very glad I'd brought the knives. You can stab vamps and keep them alive, but still make your...point.

I was finally able to separate the power of his voice from the words. Most vamps, when they can, do tricks with their voices. The words themselves hold the key. They say *beautiful*, and you see beauty. They say *terror*, and you feel afraid. But this voice had little to do with the words. It was just an overwhelming aura of power like a great white noise hum. The audience may have thought that they were hanging on every word, but the man could have recited a grocery list with similar effect.

The words were, "You saw him as the god Tezcathpoca in our opening dance. Now see him as a man." The lights had been dimming as the priest spoke, until he was left in near darkness; only the iridescent gleam of feathers showed as he moved. The light came up on the other side of the stage, revealing a man, pale skin that glowed in the lights from his bare feet to equally bare shoulder. His back was to the audience and for a moment I thought he was nude. There was nothing to break up the curve of his body from the swell of his calves, to his thighs, the tight roundness of his buttocks, the lean waist, the spread of shoulders. His hair looked black under the lights, cut so close to his head that it looked shaved. He turned slowly, revealing the barest of G-strings, a color so close to his skin that you knew the illusion of nudity was a planned effect.

His face shone unadorned like a star, starkly beautiful. He looked somehow pure and perfect, which wasn't possible. No one human was perfect. But he was pretty. A line of black hair ran down the center of his chest and stomach to vanish into the thong. Our table was close enough, and his body white enough, that I could see the thin line of hair encircling his nipples to meet that thin line down his chest like the soft arms of a T.

I actually had to shake my head to clear it. Maybe it was being celibate, or maybe there was more magic in the air than just the voice of the human servant. I looked back at the stage and knew that it was only a trick of the light that made his skin seem to glow. I looked over at Professor Dallas. She had her head bent very close to Edward, talking to him in whispers. If she saw the show almost every night, it was nothing new to her, but the lack of attention that she paid the man made me turn and search the dim tables around us. Most eyes, especially the women, were turned rapt to the stage. But not all eyes. Some were drinking, holding hands with their dates, doing other things. I turned back to the stage and just looked at him, drinking in the lines of his body. Damn, it was just me. Or rather, it was just a normal human reaction to a nearly naked and attractive man. I'd have preferred a spell. At least then I could blame someone else. My hormones, my fault. I needed more hobbies, that was it, more hobbies. That would fix everything.

The lights came up slowly until the Priest was visible once more. "It was traditional that twenty days before the great ceremony, brides would be chosen for him." I caught a glimpse of fur, and for just an instant I thought it was a line of shapeshifters in their half-human, half-beast guise. But it was men dressed in leopard skins. Not hanging loose like cloaks but as if the skins were sewn around their bodies. Some of them were too tall for the skins so that a foot or more of bare leg showed below the animal feet, or out of the clawed arms. They moved among the tables in a strangely graceful line, encased in fur with their faces framed through the open jaws of the dead animals.

A man passed within touching distance of our table, and I saw the black rosettes that decorated the golden skin more closely, and it wasn't leopard. I was spending a lot of time with St. Louis' wereleopards. I'd killed the wereleopard leader because he was trying to kill me, among other things. But I'd left the leopards without a leader, and shapeshifters without a leader are anyone's meat. So I was de facto leader until we could work something else out. I'd been learning how to forge them into a stronger unit, or pard. One of the ways you did that was sheer physical closeness, not sex, but closeness. I stared at the skin, and my hand went out without thinking. The man's movement stroked my hand over the once living fur. The spots were larger. The markings weren't as neat somehow. I watched the cat heads on the men, and the heads were more square, not the rounded almost feminine line of leopard. Jaguars, they were jaguars, which made perfect sense with the Aztec motif, but, like the bird feathers, I wondered how they'd obtained the skins, and was it legal. I knew it wasn't right. I don't believe in killing for decoration. I wear leather because I eat meat, just using the whole animal. Nothing wasted.

The man turned and looked at me. His eyes were blue, his face tanned a pale gold that matched the line of belly fur just before it turned white. The moment he looked at me energy danced down my skin like a hot breath. A shapeshifter, great. There was a time, not long ago, that that much power this close would have drawn an answering energy from me, but not this time. I sat there staring at him, and I was safe behind my shield that squeezed down a layer of energy that stood between me and all the psychic shit. I gave him innocent brown eyes, and he moved off through the tables as if I was no longer interesting. Which was fine with me.

I didn't reach out for it, but the energy came here and there from them. It would have been so much worse without the shielding. They had to be werejaguars or the costumes were like the ultimate false advertising. Somehow, this didn't strike me as a show that promised anything it couldn't deliver.

The werejaguars picked women from the audience, took them by the hand and led them towards the stage. A petite blonde was pulled from her seat giggling. A short, square woman with skin the color of tanned leather was pulled solemn-faced and didn't seem to be nearly as pleased, but she let herself be led to the stage. A taller more slender Hispanic woman was next, with long black hair that shimmered as she moved like an ebony curtain. She stumbled on the steps, and only the werejaguar's arm saved her from falling. She laughed as he steadied her, and I realized she was drunk.

A figure appeared in front of me, blocking my view of the stage. I looked up into a dark face framed by snarling jaws. The jaguar's golden glass eyes rode above the man's face, as if the dead animal were staring at me, too. The man reached a square, dark hand out to me.

I shook my head.

The hand stayed, pale palm up, waiting.

I shook my head again. "No, thanks anyway."

Dallas leaned around Edward, across the table, having to nearly crawl on it to get close to me. It stretched her body in a long line, her long ponytail pooling on the stone. Olaf's hand hovered over that spill of hair, and the look on his face was strange enough to distract me from everything else. Her voice made me look at her face instead of Olaf's. "They need someone your size and body type to round out the brides. Someone with long hair." She was smiling. "Nothing bad is going to happen." She gave me a cheerful smile that made her look even younger.

The man leaned over me and I could smell the fur and...him. Not sweat, just his scent, and that made my stomach contract, made me have to concentrate on holding my shields, because the part of me that was tied to Richard and his beast wanted to respond, wanted to spill outward and wallow in that scent. The animal impulses, true animal impulses, always threw me.

The man's voice was thickly accented, and sounded unsuited to whispering. It was a voice for shouting orders. "Do nothing that you do not wish to do, but please come to our temple."

Maybe it was the please or the accent or the absolute seriousness in his face but I believed. I still might not have gone with him, but Edward leaned into me, and said, "Tourist, think tourist." He didn't say, "Play along, Anita. Remember, we're undercover," because with a shapeshifter this close he'd hear anything that was said at the table. But Edward had said enough. I was a tourist. A tourist would go.

I gave the man my left hand and let him pull me to my feet. His hand was very warm. Some lycanthropes seem to adopt their alter ego's body temperature. Even Richard's skin grew warmer near the full moon, but that couldn't be it tonight. We were only days away from the dark of the moon, as far from the shining fullness that called the beasts as we could get. The man was just warm. Too hot for fur.

The priest in his feathers encouraged the audience to applaud as the last reluctant bride, me, joined the grouping around the nearly naked man. The werejaguar stood me on the side with the giggling blond. The smell of beer was strong enough that I knew the giggling wasn't just nervousness. Perfect.

I looked past the man, doing my best to ignore him, to the two women on the other side. The tall one with all the hair was swaying slightly on her spike heels. Her skirt was leather, and the blouse looked like a red camisole. The other woman was that solid that some people call fat, but it isn't. She was square and wore a loose black shirt over black pants. She caught my eye, and we shared a moment of discomfort. Audience participation was great as long as the audience wants to participate.

"These are your brides," the priest said, "your reward. Enjoy them."

The solid woman and I both took a step back as if it were choreographed. The blonde and the tall one with all the hair melted into his arms, cuddling and laughing. The man played to them, but it was their hands that wandered over his body. He was very careful where he touched them. I thought at first it was just fear of being sued, but there was a stiffness, a tightening of his body when their hands wandered over his bare buttocks that said he wasn't having as good a time as it looked. From the audience you'd have never noticed. He came away from them with orange-red lipstick like a wound on his pale skin and pale pink like a patch of glitter down his face.

He reached out to us, and both of us shook our heads. We took another step back, and a step closer together. Solidarity. She offered me her hand, not to shake, but to hold, and I realized she was scared, not just nervous. I was neither, just not happy. She whispered, "I'm Ramona." I gave her my name, and what seemed to matter more, held her hand. I felt like Mommy on the first day of school when the bullies are waiting.

The priest's voice came. "You are his last meal, his last caress. Do not deny him."

Ramona's face changed, grew soft. Her hand fell away from mine. The fear was gone. I called, softly, "Ramona." But she moved forward as if she never heard me. She moved into the man's arms. He kissed her with more tenderness than he'd shown the other two. She kissed him back, with a passion and a strength that made anything the other two had done seem pale and watered down. The other two women had gone to their knees on either side, either because they couldn't stand upright anymore, or the better to run their hands over both the man and the new woman. It looked like a mild version of a pornographic four-way.

He drew back from Ramona, laying a second kiss on her forehead as if she were a child. She stayed unmoving, eyes closed, face slack. It was illegal to force anyone to do anything against their will by use of magic. I looked at Ramona's empty face, waiting, waiting for what came next, all decision, all choice, washed away. If I'd been myself tonight instead of whoever the hell I was supposed to be, I'd have called them on it. I should still turn them in to the cops. But truthfully, unless they did worse, I wasn't going to turn them in if the Master of the City could help us solve the mutilation murders. If the murders stopped, a few mind-games could be overlooked.

There was a time when I wouldn't have tolerated it, when I wouldn't have looked the other way for any reason. They say everyone has their price. Once I thought I was the exception to the rule, but if it was a choice of letting this nice woman be made to do some things she didn't want to do, or seeing another crime scene, another survivor, they could have the woman. Not have in the true sense of the word, but to my knowledge mind-magic by a human servant wasn't permanent. Of course, until tonight I hadn't known a human servant could do mind-rape. I really didn't know how much danger this woman was in, and yet...and yet I would risk her, as long as nothing worse happened. If they told her to strip, all bets were off. I had rules, limits. They just weren't the same ones they'd been four years ago, or two years, or a year ago. The fact that I let them mind-rape her and didn't complain, bothered me, but not enough.

The blonde woman leaned into the man and bit his butt, not hard but enough to make him jump. His back was to the audience, so I was probably the only one who saw the anger that showed for just a moment in that handsome face.

The priest stayed on his side of the stage, as if he didn't want to distract from the show, but I knew he'd turned his attention to me. The full force of him was like pressure against my skin.

His voice. "A most reluctant bride to leave him lonely in

his hour of need." I felt his power and now that power was wedded to the words. When he said, "need," I felt need. My body tightened with it, but I could ignore it. I knew I could stand there and be unmoved, that he could do his worst and I could stand against it. But no human could have done it. Anita Blake, vamp executioner, could stand firm, but Anita Lee, undercover party-goer, well...If I just stood there, the game was up. At the very least they'd know I wasn't an ordinary tourist. Times like these are one of the reasons I hate undercover work.

I ignored the priest's rich voice and just walked toward the man. He was having trouble keeping the blonde's hand out of the front of his G-string. The other woman knelt in a pool of her own dark hair, hanging on his leg, one hand playing with the side strap of the G-string. Only Ramona stood there, face blank, hands at her sides, waiting for orders. But the priest was concentrating all his energies on me. She was safe until he finished with me.

The dark-haired woman got the strap to slide over the smooth bone of his hip, and the blonde used it as a chance to plunge her hand under the cloth. His eyes closed, head going back, body reacting automatically, even as his hand grabbed her hand and tried to pull her hand out of his pants. Apparently, she was hanging on, not hurting him exactly, but not letting go.

I doubted the club would have tolerated this level of abuse if the performer had been a woman and the audience member a man. Some forms of sexist double standards do not work in a man's favor. A woman, they would have rushed on stage and saved her, but he was a man, and he was on his own.

I touched Ramona's shoulders and moved her to one side like she was furniture. She moved where I put her, eyes still closed. Made me feel worse that she was that pliant. But one problem at a time. I put my hand on top of his and moved his hand away from the blonde's wrist. His hand didn't move at first, then he looked at me, really looked at me. His eyes were large, a soft pure gray with a circle of black around the iris like someone had used the same eye pencil to trace his eyes that they'd used on the sweep of eyebrow and dark lashes. Strange eyes. But whatever he saw in my eyes seemed to reassure him because he let go of the blonde. There's a nerve in the arm about three fingers down from the bend of the elbow. If you hit it right, it's pretty painful. I dug my fingers into her flesh, as if I'd find that nerve and drag it to the surface. I was pissed, and I wanted to hurt her. I succeeded.

She gave a small scream, her hand opened, and I was able to move her arm back, fingers digging into the nerve. She didn't struggle, just whimpered and stared up at me with large unfocused eyes, but the pain was chasing the liquor away. If I kept it up long enough, I could have sobered her up in, oh, fifteen minutes or so, if she didn't pass out first.

I spoke low, but my voice carried. The stage had great acoustics. "My turn."

The tall Hispanic woman crawled away from the man, scuttling in her tight skirt until she fell flat on her face. You have to be pretty drunk to fall from a crawling position. She got to one elbow, and her voice came thick, but panicked. "He's yours."

I drew the blonde a few steps farther away from the man, and slowly let go of her arm. I told her, "Stay." She cradled her arm against her body, huddling over it. The look she gave me was not friendly, but she didn't mouth off. I think she was afraid of me. I wasn't having a great night. First, I let the nice lady be mind-raped, then I terrorized drunken tourists. I would have said, how could the night get worse, but worse was waiting. I looked back at the nearly naked man and didn't know what to do with him.

I walked back over to him because I couldn't figure a graceful way off stage. I'd probably blown my cover as a tourist, but Edward had let me bring a gun and knives into the club. In fact, we were all loaded for bear or vampire or whatever. The bouncers, unless they were idiots, had to have seen some of the weapons. I was just not supposed to be a vamp executioner, but I've never played victim well. I should never have come on stage, but too late now.

The man and I stood facing each other, his back still to the audience. He leaned into me, breath warm against my hair. He whispered, "My hero, thank you."

I nodded, and that small movement brushed my thick hair against his face. My mouth was dry, and it was hard to swallow. My heart was suddenly beating too hard, too fast, as if I'd been running. It was a ridiculous reaction to a strange man. I was horribly aware of how close he was, how little he was wearing, and how my hands just hung at my sides because to move at all would mean to brush against him. What was the matter with me? I had not been noticing men this badly in St. Louis. Was there something in the air in New Mexico, or was it just lack of oxygen from the elevation?

He rubbed his face against my hair, whispered, "I am César." That small movement put the curve of his jaw, the skin of his neck next to my face. There was a trace of the women's perfume mixing along his face, overlaying the clean scent of his skin, but underneath it all was a sharper scent. It was the smell of warmer flesh than human, slightly musky, so rich it was almost a damp smell, as if you could bathe in the scent like water, but the water would be hot, hot as blood, hotter. The scent was so strong that I swayed, and for a second I could feel the brush of fur against my face like rough piled velvet. The sensory memory poured through me, and overwhelmed all my careful control. The power poured upward in a spill of heat along my skin. I'd managed to cut the direct links to the boys so that I was alone in my own skin, but the marks were still there, coming to the surface at odd moments, like this one. Shapeshifters always recognize each other. Their beasts always know, and though I had no beast of my own, I had a piece of Richard's. That piece reacted to César. If I'd been expecting it, I might have been able to prevent it, but it was too late now. It wasn't dangerous, just a spill of heat, pulsing along my skin, a dance of energy that didn't belong to me.

César had jerked back from me as if I'd burned him, then he smiled. It was a knowing smile like we shared a secret. He wasn't the first shapeshifter to mistake me for one of them. To my knowledge I was one of only two humans in the world that had this close a tie to a shapeshifter. The other man's tie was to a weretiger, not a werewolf, but the problems were similar. We were both part of a vampire's triumvirate, and neither of us seemed happy.

César's hands went to either side of my face, hesitating just above my skin. I knew he was feeling the push of that otherworldly energy like a veil that had to be pushed aside to touch. Except he didn't. He spilled his own power into his hands, so that he held me in a pulsing shell of warmth. It made me close my eyes, and he hadn't even touched me yet, not with his hands.

I opened my mouth to tell him not to touch me, but as I drew breath to speak his hands touched my face. I wasn't ready. He pushed his power into mine. It hit like a jolt of electricity, raising the small hairs on my body, tightening places low on my body, raising gooseflesh in a wash down my skin. The power flowed towards César like a flower turning towards the sun. I couldn't stop it. The best I could do was ride the power instead of letting it ride me.

He bent his face towards me, still cradling my face between his hands. I put my own hands on top of his as if I was going to hold on. Power poured from his mouth as he hovered over my lips. The power ran through my body and spilled out of half-parted lips like a hot wind. Our mouths met and the power flowed into each of us, mingling as it brushed like two great cats rubbing furred sides along each other's bodies. The warmth grew to heat, until it almost hurt to stay tied to his lips, as if any second now our flesh would burn into each other, melting through skin, muscle, bone, until we fell into the center of each other like molten metal cutting through layers of silk.

The energy had turned sexual, as it usually did...for me. Embarrassing but true. We drew back from the kiss at the same time, blinking at each other like sleepwalkers awakened too early. He gave a nervous laugh and leaned into me as if to kiss me again, but I put a hand on his chest, and held him away. I could feel his heart thudding against my palm. I could suddenly feel the blood racing in his body. My eyes were drawn to the big pulse in his throat. I watched that rapid rise and fall in the side of his neck as if it were some sort of jewel, something to watch sparkle and glitter in the lights. My mouth was suddenly dry, and it wasn't sex. I actually stepped into him, pressed my body down the front of his, brought my face close to his neck and that jumping beat of life. I wanted to go down on that soft skin, sink teeth into his flesh, taste what lay beneath. I knew with a knowledge that was not mine that his blood would be hotter than a human's. Not warm but hot, a scalding rush of life to warm cold flesh.

I had to close my eyes, turn my head, step away with my hands over my eyes. I had no direct link to either of the men, but I held their power in me. Richard's burning warmth, and Jean-Claude's cold hunger. For a space of heartbeats I had wanted to feed on César. This when I had walled up the marks, boarded them up, chained them, locked them with everything I had. When the marks were open between the three of us, the desires that ran through me, the things that I thought, were too horrible or maybe just too alien. Not for the first time I wondered what piece of me each of them held in their bodies. What dark desire or strange urge did I leave behind? If I ever talked to either of them again, maybe I'd ask, or then again, maybe I wouldn't.

*Special sneak preview from*

# NARCISSUS IN CHAINS

**LAURELL K. HAMILTON**

COMING IN OCTOBER 2001

The bedroom was empty when he kicked the door shut behind us. I didn't know if the living room had been empty or not. I couldn't remember anything but Richard's eyes from the kitchen to the bedroom. Every room might have been empty for all I'd seen.

We kissed just inside the door; my hands were full of the rich thickness of his hair, the firm warmth of his neck. I explored his face with my hands, my mouth, tasted, teased, caressed, just his face.

He drew back from my mouth enough to say, "If I don't sit down, I'm going to fall down, my knees are weak."

I laughed, full-throated, and said, "Then put me down."

He half-walked, half-staggered to the bed, laying me on it, going to his knees beside it. He was laughing as he crawled onto the bed. He lay beside me, his knees hanging over the side of the bed, though since he was tall enough that his feet actually touched the floor when he lay like that, maybe hanging wasn't the right word. We lay beside each other on the bed, laughing softly, not touching.

We turned our heads to look at each other at the same moment. His eyes sparkled with the laughter, his whole face almost shining with it. I reached out and traced the lines of laughter around his mouth. The laughter began to fade as soon as I touched him, his eyes filling up with something darker, more serious, but no less precious. He rolled onto his side. The movement put my hand along the side of his face. He rubbed his face into my hand, eyes closed, lips half-parted.

I rolled onto my stomach and moved toward him, my hand still on his face. He opened his eyes, watching me crawl toward him. I propped myself up on hands and knees and watched his eyes as I leaned in toward his mouth. There was eagerness there, but there was also something else, something fragile. Did my eyes mirror that look, half-eager, half-fearful, wanting, afraid to want, needing, and afraid to need?

My mouth hovered over his, our lips touching, delicate as butterflies blown by a warm summer wind, touching, not touching, sliding along each other, gliding away. His hand grabbed the back of my neck, forced my mouth to press against his, hard, firm. He used tongue and lips to force my mouth open. I opened to him and we took turns exploring each other's mouth. He came to his knees, hand still pressed to the back of my neck, our mouths still locked together. He drew back, crawling backward to the head of the bed, leaving me kneeling alone in the center of the bed. He reached under the covers, drew out pillows, propped himself up, watching me. There was something almost decadent with him naked, propped up, watching me.

I knelt looking back at him, having a little trouble focusing, thinking. I finally managed to say, "What's wrong?"

"Nothing," he said, voice deep, lower than normal. It wasn't the growl of his beast; it was a peculiarly male sound.

"I want to run my beast through you, Anita."

For a split second, I thought it was a euphemism, then I realized he meant exactly what he'd said. "Richard, I don't know."

"I know you don't like otherworldly stuff during sex, but Anita…" He settled into the pillows in a strange smoothing motion that somehow reminded me that he wasn't human, "I felt your beast. It rolled through me."

Just hearing it out loud took a little of the glow off for me. I slumped back against the bed, still on my knees, but no longer upright, hands limp in my lap. "Richard, I haven't had time to think this through. I don't know how I feel about it yet."

"It's not all bad, Anita. Some of it can be wondrous."

This from the man who had hated his beast for the entire time I'd known him; but I didn't say it out loud, I just looked at him.

He smiled. "I know how strange that sounds coming from me."

I looked at him harder.

He laughed, settling lower on the pillows until he was sprawled in front of me. One leg bent up so he wouldn't touch me, but close enough that I could have touched him. He lay there unself-consciously nude, which I'd seen before, but it was more than that. He seemed bathed in a comfortableness that was rare for Richard. I'd seen it at the lupanar, that he'd accepted his beast, but it was more than that, he'd accepted himself.

"What do you want from me, Richard?"

This was his cue to get serious, to demand I be less bloodthirsty, or a half dozen other impossible things. He didn't. "I want this," he said, and I felt the prickling rush of his power a second before it passed through me like a warm ghost.

I shuddered with it. "I don't know, Richard, I don't know if this is a good idea." It would have sounded better if my voice hadn't had a tremble in it.

I expected him to ask, or talk, but he didn't. I felt his power like a brush of thunder a second before it smashed into me. I had a second of panic, a moment to wonder if his beast and mine would claw me apart, then his power rubbed through me like a velvet glove. My beast rose as if from a great, warm, wet depth, up, up, to meet the warm, burning rush of Richard's energy. He pushed his beast through me and I could feel it, impossibly huge, the brush of fur so deep inside me that I cried out. I felt his beast as if it had crawled inside me and was caressing things from the inside that his hands would never have touched. My power seemed less certain than his, less solid. But it rose around the hard, muscled fur like velvet mist, swirling through his power, through my own body. Until it felt as if something huge was growing inside me, something I'd never felt before, swelling inside me. It felt larger than my body, as if I couldn't hold it inside myself, like a cup filled to the brim with something hot and scalding, but the liquid kept pouring in, and still I held it, held it, held it, until it burst over me, through me, out of me, in a roar of power that turned the world golden and slow, drew my body to its knees, curved my back, sent my hands clawing at the air trying to hold onto something, anything, while my body spilled apart, and remade itself on the bed. For a space of labored heartbeats I thought he'd brought on the change, and I had slipped my skin for real, but it wasn't that. I felt like I was floating and only gradually felt my body again. I lay on my back, my knees folded under me, hands limp at my sides, so relaxed it was like being drugged.

I felt the bed move under me, and a moment—or a minute—later, Richard appeared above me. He was on all fours, looming over me, and I had trouble focusing on his face. He cradled my face, staring into my eyes, while I tried to look at him. "Anita, are you all right?"

I laughed then, slow and lazy. "Help me get my knees straightened out, and I'll be fine."

He helped me straighten my legs, and even then all I wanted to do was just lie there. "What did you do to me?"

He lay down beside me, propped on one elbow. "I brought you using the beasts."

I blinked at him, licked my lips, and tried to think of an intelligent question, gave up, and settled for what I wanted to know. "Is it always like that between lycanthropes?"

"No," he said, and leaned over me, until his face filled my vision. "No, only a true lupa, or a true Nimir-ra, can respond to my Ulfric the way you just did."

I touched his chest enough to back him up so I could see his face clearly. "You've never done that with anyone before?"

He looked down then, a curtain of his hair sliding over his face, hiding his face from me. I pushed his hair back so I could see that nearly perfect profile. "Who?" I asked.

Heat washed up his neck and face. I wasn't sure I'd ever seen him blush before. "It was Raina, wasn't it?"

He nodded. "Yes."

I let his hair fall back in place and lay there for a few seconds thinking about it. Then I was laughing, laughing, and couldn't stop.

He was back at my shoulder, peering down at me. "Anita?"

The laughter faded as I looked into his worried eyes. "When you forced Raina to give you up all those years ago, did you know that she was the only one that could do this with you?"

He nodded, face solemn. "Raina pointed out the down side of not being her pet."

I took his hand and slid it down the front of my satin shorts. His fingertips found the wetness that had soaked through the satin, and I didn't have to guide his hand anymore. He cupped that big hand of his over my groin, and the cloth was soaked through. He traced fingertips across my inner thigh and the skin was wet, wet down to my knees.

"How did you give it up?" My voice came out in a whisper.

His finger slid up the inside of my thigh, in the hollow just below. He leaned in to kiss me as his finger slid slowly upward across the moist skin under the wet satin. His mouth stayed just above mine, so close that a sharp breath would have made us touch. He spoke, his breath warm on my skin as his finger caressed the edge of me. "No amount of pleasure was worth her price."

Two things happened at once; he kissed me, and his finger slid inside of me. I screamed against his mouth, back arching, fingernails digging into his shoulder as his finger found that small spot, and thrust over it, and over it, until he brought me again; the world had soft, white edges like seeing through gauze.

I felt the bed move, but couldn't focus, couldn't see, wasn't sure I cared what was happening. Hands fumbled at my shorts. I blinked up to see Richard kneeling over me. He slid my shorts down my legs, spread my legs, and knelt between them. He leaned over me, raising the satin camisole, baring my breasts. He ran his hands across them, made me writhe, then rolled his hands down the line of my body, his hands gripping my thighs, bringing me in a harsh jerk against his body.

The moment he rubbed against the outside of me, I felt the rubbery latex of the condom. I looked up at his face, and asked, "How did you know?"

He moved so that his lower body was lying between my legs, but still pressed against the outside of my body. Most of his weight was supported by his arms like a modified push-up position. "Do you really think Jean-Claude would warn me about the arduer and not warn me that you weren't on birth control?"

"Good point," I said.

"No," he said, "this is." I felt the movement of his hips seconds before he thrust inside me, in one powerful movement that drove sounds from my mouth, somewhere between a scream, and a shout.

He lowered his head enough to see my face. I lay gasping under him, but whatever he saw there reassured him, because he arched his back, his face looking somewhere in the distance, and drew himself out of me, slowly, inch by inch, until I made small noises. He drew himself out until he was barely touching inside me. I gazed down the length of my body to see him stretched hard and ready. He'd always been careful of me, because he wasn't small; that one first thrust had been more force than he'd ever allowed himself. He filled me up, hit that point deep inside that was either pain or pleasure. I saw his back and hips flex a second before he thrust into me again. I watched him thrust into me, saw every inch of him plunge into me, until it bowed my back, my neck, and I couldn't watch because I was writhing underneath him, my hands scrambling at the bedspread, digging fingers into the covers.

He drew himself out of me again, and I stopped him with a hand on his stomach. "Wait, wait." I was having trouble breathing.

"It's not hurting you, I can tell by your face, your eyes, your body."

I swallowed, took a shaky breath, and said, "No, it's not hurting me. It feels wonderful, but you've always been so careful, even when I asked you not to be. What's changed?"

He looked down at me, his hair falling around his face like a silken frame. "I was always afraid of hurting you before. But I felt your beast."

"I haven't changed yet, Richard, we don't know for sure."

"Anita," he said softly, and I knew he was chiding me. Maybe it was a case of the lady protesting too much, but still…

"I'm still human, Richard, I haven't changed yet."

He leaned over me, his hair gliding around my face as he kissed me gently on the cheek. "Even before the first full moon, we can take more damage. The change has already begun, Anita."

I pushed against his chest until he drew back enough for me to see his face. "You've always been holding back, haven't you?"

"Yes," he said.

I searched his face and saw such need in his eyes, and I knew why he'd been so angry at Gregory. He'd said that he almost regretted not making me his lupa, now that he'd seen me be Nimir-ra, but it was more than that. I looked into his brown eyes in the spill of early morning light and knew that he'd wanted me to be what he was, even though he hated it, that at some level he'd been tempted to make me his lupa for real. Somewhere in the lovemaking, where he had to be so careful, he'd thought of it, more than once. It was there in his eyes, his face. He started to look away as if he could feel that I saw it all, but he made himself look back, meet my gaze. He was almost defiant.

"How careful have you been of me, Richard?"

He did look away then, using his hair as a shield. I reached through that thick hair to touch his face, to turn him to look at me. "Richard, how careful have you been of me?"

There was something close to pain in his eyes. He whispered, "Very."

I held his face between my hands. "You don't have to be careful anymore."

A look of soft wonderment crossed his face, and he bent his head down, and we kissed, kissed as we had earlier, prodding, exploring, taking turns at thrusting into each other. He drew slowly back from the kiss and I felt the tip of him touch my opening. I stared down the length of our bodies so I could watch as his body flexed above me, and he thrust himself inside me harder this time, quicker. It brought my breath in a soundless scream.

"Anita…"

I opened my eyes, not realizing I'd closed them. I gazed up at him. "Don't be careful anymore, Richard, don't be careful."

He smiled, gave me a quick kiss, then he was back, arched above me, and this time he didn't stop. He thrust every inch of himself into me as hard and as fast as he could. The sound of flesh into flesh became a constant sound, a wet hammering. I realized it hadn't been just his size that made him careful, but his strength. He could have bench-pressed the bed we lay on, and that strength lay not just in his arms, or back, but in his legs, his thighs, in the body he was pressing inside me, over and over again. For the first time ever, I began to appreciate the full power of him.

I'd felt the strength in his hands, his arms, when he held me, but it was nothing to this. He made of our bodies one body, one pounding, sweating, soaking, drenching piece of flesh. I was vaguely aware that it did hurt, that I was bruising, and I didn't care.

I called out his name as my body tightened around his, squeezing, and I spasmed underneath him, my body slamming against the bed, not from Richard's thrusts, but from the power of the orgasm itself; screams spilled from my throat as my body rocked underneath him. It felt good, better than almost anything, but it was almost violence, almost pain, almost frightening. Somewhere in the midst of it all I was aware that he came, too. He screamed my name, but held his place, while I continued to writhe and fight underneath him. It wasn't until I lay quiet that he allowed himself to collapse on top of me, slightly to one side so my face wouldn't be pressed into his chest.

We lay in a sweating, breathless heap, waiting for our hearts to slow enough to speak. He found his voice first. "Thank you, thank you for trusting me."

I laughed. "You're thanking me." I raised his hand to my mouth and kissed the palm, then rested his hand against my face. "Trust me, Richard, it was my pleasure."

He laughed, that rich throaty sound that is purely male, and purely sexual. "We're going to need another shower."

"Whichever of us can walk first can have the first shower," I said.

He laughed and hugged me. I wasn't even sure my legs would work enough to shower. Maybe a bath.

Roy Zipstein

**LAURELL K. HAMILTON** is a full-time writer and mother. Her bestselling Anita Blake, Vampire Hunter novels include *Obsidian Butterfly*, *Blue Moon*, *Burnt Offerings*, *The Killing Dance*, *Bloody Bones*, *The Lunatic Cafe*, *Circus of the Damned*, *The Laughing Corpse*, and *Guilty Pleasures*. She lives in a suburb of St. Louis with her family.

᾿ Her new Anita Blake, Vampire Hunter novel, *Narcissus in Chains*, is out in October 2001.

Her official website is: www.lkhamilton.com

Visit Berkley and Ace Books online: www.penguinputnam.com

# FREE

Roy Zipstein

"With a heroine as sharp as a stake and slick as a silver bullet, Laurell K. Hamilton sucks you into her fascinating world like a vampire's kiss."
—J. D. Robb

"Erotic…edgy…red-hot entertainment."
—Jayne Ann Krentz

**MEET ANITA BLAKE**—a woman with definite love/hate relationship problems with creatures of the night—and enter the seductive world of *New York Times* bestselling author Laurell K. Hamilton…

With this free introductory booklet, you can experience the wild nightlife of Anita Blake in excerpts from *Guilty Pleasures*, *The Lunatic Cafe*, and *Obsidian Butterfly*…

Get a special sneak preview of Laurell K. Hamilton's new Anita Blake, Vampire Hunter novel, *Narcissus in Chains*, a Berkley hardcover, coming in October 2001…

Eavesdrop on a revealing interview with the vampire author…and follow Laurell on a tour of vampire haunts from Tennessee to St. Louis to New Mexico!

**BERKLEY    ACE**
Members of Penguin Putnam Inc.
www.penguinputnam.com

She glanced at Ry, who looked as dumbfounded as she felt.

Ian looked at her. Pain flashed across his face, though he hid it quickly. "The three of us. You made your choice—you love him, don't you?"

"I do."

He nodded, and bent to insert the key into the lock that held her door closed. "So that's it. I'm saving you because I love you." The chain that held her door closed rattled softly as he worked the lock. "And I'll save him . . . because I love you." He shrugged and avoided her eyes.

"You sacrificed yourself to help us? Me?"

"We don't have time to talk," he rasped.

Something inside her hurt at that moment. She wished she had been able to love him. She wished she could be two people so that she could be with Ian and with Ry without betraying either of them, or that she had never met Ian, or that she could take his pain away. The magnitude of what he'd done for her unrolled before her in the few moments that he struggled with the lock that kept her caged. "Why did you come here?" she asked him.

Her lock clattered open and the chain rattled to the floor. Ian immediately hurried to Ry's cage and began working on that lock. Kait crawled out of her cage and stretched.

"You mean right here? Or to the Dragons?"

"Both."

"I figured out a way I could get to the Mirror of Souls. And I knew you needed it. So since you had . . ." Another shrug. "Since you had someone else, I decided I was free to go. I offered my services to the Sabirs, but especially to Crispin—I told him lies about how much I wanted to get even with you, and he put me in charge of the combined Sabir and Galweigh forces. I . . . I did some things I don't want to think about in order to convince him that I was what I said I was. People died at my word and by my hand. They weren't innocents, but they were innocent of the things I said they did." Ry's lock opened, and Ian backed up so that his half-brother could free himself. "Come with me. We have a ways to go to get to the Mirror, and not much time."

He led them out of the beautiful arched room into a corridor. In the darkness, only the pale glimmer of moonlight shining through skylights illuminated it.

"This way."

They followed him, silent for the moment. Kait could hear movement within some of the rooms they passed, and once she and Ry hid in a room while Ian stood in front of the door, his guard's uniform rendering him effectively invisible. No one spoke again until he led them down a long, twisting staircase into a vault beneath the white city. He took a key and opened one door, then pressed a complex combination of switches to open the next door.

"In here."

Kait and Ry followed him into a narrow room lit by hundreds of tiny pebbles embedded in the ceiling; the Mirror of Souls sat on a dais in the center of the room, dark and seemingly dead.

"How do we get it out of here?" Kait asked.

"I have a friend in a closed carriage waiting at the south gate of the Citadel. I sent him the message just before I came to get you. He'll wait for us for a full day."

"Then all we have to do is figure out how to carry it past the Dragons without them seeing us."

"I'd hoped you could shield it the way you did when we escaped the *Wind Treasure*," Ian said.

Kait looked at Ry. "I can do that. Ry and I are both weak—it might take some time to get it right."

Ian looked from one of them to the other. "Hurry. Someone will be along to check on this thing within the station. I can kill him, but the moment he doesn't report in, more will be on the way."

asmal told Dafril nothing that he wanted to know, but he was no longer able to feign indifference. Through the early part of the torture, he'd placed himself in the meditative trance he would have used to summon magic, had he not been shielded from it. He'd withstood terrible things by standing apart from his body and watching what was done to him as if he were only a distant and uninterested observer.

Now, though, the pain had become too much, and he'd lost the trance. He was once again entirely in his body, and bleeding from a multitude of cuts, and scarred from burns with a branding iron. The pain was riveting; he couldn't pull himself away from Dafril's soft, amused voice any longer.

"Suddenly I feel that you're with me again," Dafril said. "That's good. That should speed up this process enormously. I'll have you know that I've broken hundreds of your sort, young Falcon—hundreds. Stronger men than you, and men who had full control of Matrin's magic. You'll tell me what I want to know."

Dafril had kept his distance, and kept to the left of Hasmal. The talisman on his right finger still waited, but Dafril had never moved within the slight range of his bound hand. He had to get him close—

Searing pain ripped into his ribs, and he heard his skin sizzle. He screamed and fought against the restraints that bound him.

Dafril sighed. "You see? This hurts a lot, and you aren't as brave or as strong as you think you are. So help me out, and I'll help you. Tell me how you and your friends are stealing the souls of my colleagues."

Hasmal's mind raced. He thought of half a dozen lies, but all of them were improbable and sounded weak even to him—and if he told Dafril anything, he knew the Dragon would just keep torturing him, making sure that what he said at the beginning matched what he would say when he was more desperate.

He turned his face away.

"Look at me."

He stared off to his right, trying to think of something that might save him, that might get Dafril within his range.

"Look at me, damn you."

The searing pain again, this time high on the inside of his thigh.

He screamed and writhed, but kept his face turned from Dafril. It seemed to help.

Dafril said, "I can come around to that side, you idiot. You won't win anything this way."

Hasmal's heart leaped. Yes, he thought. Do come around.

Dafril did, carrying a knife. "Look, you—I can carve out your eyes and your ears, cut off your nose, rip off your balls, or skin the flesh from your body if I have to. The only part of you that I need to have in working order is your tongue."

Hasmal met his gaze defiantly, and managed a grin. So this was courage—being trapped and terrified and holding fast because he loved Alarista, and because cowardice would betray her.

He wondered if that was the difference between courage and cowardice—if brave men loved someone outside of themselves while cowards loved only their own lives. If that were true, then all men might be cowards sometimes and heroes at others. Then he wondered if all courage trembled inside—if all of it felt so thin and fragile, so ready to tatter and blow away in the next faint breeze—or if there was a better sort of courage that filled the belly with reckless fire and protected the mind from terror. If any of that sort of courage existed, he wished he could have some, because he was so scared he feared his heart would burst through his chest.

"Stubborn bastard. I'd cooperate if I were you."

"You aren't me," Hasmal whispered.

"What was that?" Dafril leaned closer so that he could hear what Hasmal had said.

Yes, he thought. "I'll tell you," he whispered, his voice even softer than before.

Dafril stepped in close and leaned all the way over Hasmal. "Louder," he said. "Say it louder."

And that was close enough. Hasmal rested his index finger against Dafril's leg. He felt the slight vibration as the talisman popped away from his skin and burrowed through the cloth of Dafril's breeches.

In a moment, Alarista and Dùghall would see him through Dafril's eyes. Dùghall would enter Dafril and pull his soul out and trap it in one of the tiny soul-mirrors that waited on the floor of the tent. And Hasmal would be saved—if he could just hold on until they could reach him.

"We found a way to make our own Mirror of Souls," he whispered.

Dafril's eyes narrowed, and he ran his thumb along the bloody edge of the knife. "Really? Tell me more."

# Chapter 55

They lugged the Mirror of Souls through the dark underpassages of the Citadel of the Gods, breathless, frightened, yet exhilarated, too. Kait had to fight the urge to shout, to scream defiance at the Dragons who went unaware about their business in the white streets above her head. We have it, she thought. We have it, and we're going to get away with it, and we're going to destroy you.

"How much farther?" Ry, the strongest of the three of them, carried most of the Mirror's weight; he'd positioned the artifact with two of its petals resting on the small of his back and he gripped one petal in each hand. She and Ian followed him, balancing a tripod leg each. They seemed to Kait to be moving quickly, but they'd been in those dark passages for a long time anyway.

"Can you see a fork in the passageway ahead of us yet?" Ian asked.

"It goes off in three directions."

"We'll take the left corridor. The passage will start rising immediately and branch again. The right branch comes out in a guardhouse at the Citadel's service gate. We'll have to kill the guard, but my friend and his carriage will be parked behind the stables across the street."

"I can already smell outside air," Kait said.

She saw Ry nod. "I do, too."

The picked up their pace until they were running. It was an unconscious action born of fear and anticipation, but it was dangerous, too. Hurrying, their breathing became louder and their attention too focused on the simple mechanics of not falling down while carrying their burden. "We have to slow down," Kait said, pulling backward on her leg of the tripod.

Both men slowed without a word.

Kait heard voices ahead. "Who is likely to be coming through here at this time of day?" she asked Ian.

"Soldiers . . . gardeners . . . servants . . . Could be anyone."

"We'll have to kill them," Ry said.

"Maybe not," Ian said. The corridor they were in was pierced at right angles by regular intersections with other, similar corridors. "We can just move aside and hope they don't notice us."

"And if they do?" Ry asked.

Kait sighed. "Then we'll have to kill them. But we'll all be better off if we don't." Them included, she thought. She had no stomach for the murder of innocent gardeners or serving girls.

They moved into the first corridor to their right and stood in the shadows, not moving and barely breathing. They saw a light flickering from ahead of where they'd been walking. They waited, and the voices grew louder.

". . . and I told Marthe I was going to quit and find a job slopping hogs if I couldn't find nothing better," a man's voice said. "Hogs is friendlier than these bastards."

"A hog'll rip your arm off and eat it in front of you, you ain't careful," a woman's voice answered. "Hogs is mean."

"And these people's meaner. You're fresh from the country—you haven't seen what I've seen. But you mark my

words, Lallie, they'll be dug under your skin and sucking
the life out of you before you're here a week. Find something else."

"If that's such good advice, why ain't you already taken
it?"

The pair drew even with Kait's hiding place and she
watched them. Their torch illuminated a tired-looking man
of perhaps forty, slouch-shouldered and with thinning hair
and a fresh-scrubbed young woman with a pert smile and a
bounce in her step.

"Because the bastards pay in good gold, and gold's hard
to come by these days."

The girl flashed a broad grin up at the man and laughed.
"As hard for me as for you, I reckon, and I swear I'm tired
of being paid in eggs and promises. I guess I can wash
clothes for bastards good as I can for my neighbors."

They were past, then, and Kait's heart slowed its knock-
ing in her chest.

"I reckon you can. I just hope you don't mind paying a
high price for your gold wage."

Kait wanted to tell the girl, *Listen to him, you idiot.* Instead, she contented herself with the thought that she held
the Dragons' downfall in her hands. Maybe, if Lallie
wouldn't save herself, Kait could save her. Maybe.

The voices died away to silence at last, and Ry and Kait
and Ian got back under way.

The guardhouse proved to be close, and Ian proved to be
right in his description of what they would find there. A
guard stood, his back to them, watching a few boys playing
ball in the alley he guarded. There was no traffic. There were
no pedestrians.

Ian drew his knife, slipped behind the guard, jammed a
leather gag into the man's mouth, and slammed him on the
back of the head with the pommel of his knife. The man fell
like a dropped bag of rocks. Kait saw that he was still

breathing. Ian carefully removed the leather gag and stood staring down at the man.

"I thought you were going to kill him," Ry said.

"I've done more than my share of killing since I came here." He looked bleak when he said it. "He didn't see us, he didn't hear us, and he won't be able to tell anyone which way we went or what we did."

Ry nodded. "I'm not complaining."

"Where's your carriage?"

Ian said, "Stand here a moment." He strolled across the street, to all appearances the guard in the guardhouse stepping out for a moment to take a look at something interesting. When he came back, Kait heard wheels rattle, and an instant later, a large black funeral carriage drawn by four black horses rolled into view. It stopped in front of the guardhouse and Kait, Ry, and Ian dragged the Mirror of Souls into the darkened interior and followed it in.

The carriage lurched forward.

"Where are we going?" Kait asked. She couldn't believe that they were free.

"Galweigh House," Ian said softly. "It's the last place anyone will think to look for us."

# About the Author

Holly Lisle, born in 1960, has been writing science fiction full time since November of 1992. Prior to that, she worked as an advertising representative, a commercial artist, a guitar teacher, a restaurant singer, and for ten years as a registered nurse specializing in emergency and intensive care. Originally from Salem, Ohio, she has also lived in Alaska, Costa Rica, Guatemala, North Carolina, Georgia, and Florida. She and Matt are raising three children and several cats. Her Secret Texts series concludes with *Courage of Falcons* available now in trade paperback.

# VISIT WARNER ASPECT ONLINE!

## THE WARNER ASPECT HOMEPAGE
You'll find us at: www.twbookmark.com then by clicking on Science Fiction and Fantasy.

## NEW AND UPCOMING TITLES
Each month we feature our new titles and reader favorites.

## AUTHOR INFO
Author bios, bibliographies and links to personal websites.

## CONTESTS AND OTHER FUN STUFF
Advance galley giveaways, autographed copies, and more.

## THE ASPECT BUZZ
What's new, hot and upcoming from Warner Aspect: awards news, bestsellers, movie tie-in information . . .